The natural guide to
Medicinal Herbs and Plants

The natural guide to Medicinal Herbs and Plants

FRANTIŠEK STARÝ

ILLUSTRATED BY HANA STORCHOVÁ

IMPORTANT NOTICE

This book is primarily to be read as a source of interesting information and not as a practical guide to self-medication. As is the case with all medicines, it is strongly recommended that a doctor's advice is sought before administration for any medical condition.

It cannot be over-emphasised that many plants are poisonous, some extremely so, and many which are beneficial in small doses can also be harmful if taken to excess or for long periods. Plants which are highly toxic or have parts which must not be used due to the risk of poisoning (possibly fatal) are marked thus . Other plants which may have unpleasant effects in specific circumstances appear with a warning at the end of the text.

All herbal infusions and decoctions should be freshly prepared and should certainly be used within twelve hours of making up.

BARNES
&NOBLE
BOOKS
NEW YORK

Text by František Starý
Illustrated by Hana Storchová
Translated by Olga Kuthanová
Graphic design by Miloš Lang

This edition published 1998 by
Barnes & Noble, Inc.
by arrangement with
Aventinum Publishers, Prague,
Czech Republic

1998 Barnes & Noble Books

M 10 9 8 7 6 5

ISBN 0-88029-828-6
Printed in the Czech Republic
3/15/27/51-06

CONTENTS

FOREWORD

Many books have been written about medicinal plants: there is a vast wealth of information available already (why even A. Tschirch's classic work *'Handbuch der Pharmakognosie'* written at the beginning of this century contains almost four thousand pages!). The aim of this book is to summarize that information in the light of current scientific knowledge.

Each illustrated plant species is accompanied by a brief botanical description and instructive drawings, to aid identification. The text is based on the author's experience of many years and takes into account the important works of world scientific literature, e. g. the outstanding textbook *'Lehrbuch der Phytotherapie'* by R. F. Weiss, the latest, sixth edition of which was published in 1985. For practical reasons the botanical terminology is according to the 13th edition of *'Zander Handwörterbuch der Pflanzennamen'* of 1983. *Plants that are extremely potent and poisonous even in small doses are marked with a warning symbol.*

This book is not intended as a practical manual for self-medication. Medicinal plants are drugs and cannot be used at will. A reliable diagnosis can be made only by a physician and that is why professional advice should *always* be sought before dosing yourself, or for that matter anyone else, with herbal medicines. Only in this way can you safely make use of the beneficial effects of the natural remedies which have been available to us all for centuries.

THE IMPORTANCE OF MEDICINAL PLANTS

Medicinal plants are considerable in number and economically important. They contain active constituents which are used in the treatment of many different diseases. Besides being used as direct remedies, they are also used in the pharmaceutical, cosmetics, perfumery, and food industries.

The pharmaceutical industry mainly uses plants that contain known medicinally effective chemical substances that are either extremely costly or impossible to produce synthetically. The active constituents are first isolated from the plants and then used in the manufacture of drugs. Because this requires large quantities of raw material, large-scale commercial crop production is necessary. Demand can occasionally be met by collecting in the wild.

The following are a few examples. Digoxin, the main ingredient of many preparations used in the treatment of heart disease, is obtained from the crude version of the drug, which is extracted from the fermented leaves of the Common Foxglove. Because digoxin is present in the crude drug in only tenths of one percent many tons of the substance must be processed to obtain the necessary quantities.

The substances used in pharmaceutical preparations for treating liver diseases are the flavonolignans from the fruits of Milk Thistle. In order to obtain the tons of achenes or seedpods necessary for that purpose, Milk Thistle is cultivated on vast tracts of land, as far away as South America, for the needs of manufacturers in Europe. Scented Mayweed is also grown there because European growers do not produce enough to meet the demand for this highly prized herb with a wide range of medicinal uses.

There is not enough space here to list all such examples. Organized collecting in the wild provides, among other things, the natural substances used in preparations for the treatment of various circulatory disorders, for example, aescin which is obtained from the fruits of Horse Chestnut. Like digoxin, many tons of the raw material are required. The same is true of rutin, obtained from *Sophora japonica,* in which case the crude drug is imported from China. Aromatic plants of the Mediterranean region, e. g. Common Sage, are also gathered by organized collectors.

Nowadays some three hundred species of medicinal and aromatic plants are used worldwide in the pharmaceutical, food, cosmetics and perfumery industries, and the medicinal substances of others may likewise be used as flavouring agents and natural pigments.

In addition to medicinal plants there are many more that are used as such, by themselves, in various forms such as herbal teas or alcohol extracts and tinctures. A further seven hundred species or so worldwide is a sober estimate, and this is without taking into account traditional home remedies.

European folk medicine currently uses some two hundred species of native medicinal plants to treat a wide range of common diseases. Many are obtained by collecting in the wild, a lesser number are grown on small plots. They are bought by large pharmacies or other marketing organizations for processing and these organizations either market them further or make them up into simple medicines which are sold in pharmacies and specialist shops. Only a negligible quantity serves collectors and growers for their own use.

People often ask if this ancient tradition of herbal medicine is outdated. The reply is an unequivocal 'No'. Man has always been highly dependent on

Paracelsus' coat-of-arms consisted of a silver renaissance escutcheon, or shield, with the Hohenheim coat-of-arms in the centre encircled by eight black crosses. The crest, mantlings, and Hohenheim coat-of-arms are coloured gold, blue and silver.

nature. In the early period of his existence he did not understand much of what went on around him. Ignorance bred superstition, and this was reflected in every human act, including the treatment of disease. The search for a cure was not only the instinct of self-preservation but also self-protection. These first efforts to ensure a continued existence on earth served as the foundation of medicine and healing. The only place man could find these medicines was his environment. He could not explain the reasons behind each plant's different effect on the human system, and that is how myths and superstitions came into being. The conflict between these and scientific knowledge is one that runs through the entire history of mankind. The ancient cultures of China, India and Egypt followed the arts of healing and medicine and with the Moorish school of medicine shaped views in Europe better and more clearly than the unenlightened Middle Ages. Not until the Renaissance was the way opened again to reason and the quest for knowledge.

Throughout history medicinal plants have figured highly in the life of man: they were always of paramount importance in the treatment of disease for the common people as well as those in power. They cannot now be seen as useless or naive; on the contrary it is necessary to keep alive all the knowledge there is about them: in the Bible, volumes by ancient scholars, and old monastery manuscripts.

The 15th century marked the beginning of the spread of knowledge about medicinal plants and medical practice, in the form of compilations called

Illumination from a 12th century German manuscript.

Miniature of a monastery apothecary from the 13th century manuscript *Chirurgia* by Roger von Salerno.

herbals. These are often presented without critical editing but are, nonetheless, remarkable and important works in their scope and comprehensiveness. For instance, the well-known work *'Der Gart der Gesundheit' (Der Kleine Hortus sanitatis)*, first published in 1485, contains accounts of four hundred and thirty-five species of medicinal plants. *'Der grosse Hortus sanitatis'*, published somewhat later (1491), contains accounts of five hundred and twenty-nine species of medicinal plants and their products. The most renowned authors of herbals were Otto Brunfels (1489—1534), Hieronymus (Jerome) Bock (1498—1554) and Leonhard Fuchs or Fuchsius (1501—1566), rightfully known today as the fathers of botany. They were followed by J. T. Tabernaemontanus († 1590), P. A. Matthioli (1501—1577), and V. Cordus (1515—1544) whose works still served as a main source of reference for physicians in the 19th century. The greatest physician of Europe at that time was Phillippus Aureolus Paracelsus, born Theophrastus Bombastus von Hohenheim (1493—1541), whose study of medicinal plants gave rise to the belief that nature is a vast pharmacy and that there is no plant on this earth that could not be used for the treatment of some disease or other.

The era of the 'herbalists' coincided with the discovery of the New World between 1492 and 1500. In the year 1500 Alvarez Cabral landed on the coast of Brazil and claimed it for Portugal. This marked the beginning not only of the avid acquisition of gold but of the natural wealth of the New World as well. Then, as now, Europeans were interested in all forms of plants and their uses. Thus began the introduction of newly imported plant species to Europe's botanical gardens, and medicinal products, such as balsam and tropical drugs, to its apothecaries.

Up until the mid-19th century there was no doubting the absolute supremacy of natural *'materia medica'* from plants in the production of medicines, as well as directly in medical practice. This is evidenced by the equipment of pharmacies from the sober Middle Ages to the ornamental Baroque. This included a great variety of jars and vessels for storing drugs and medicines made from them. In the beginning the furnishings and equipment of pharmacies were very simple, even somewhat Spartan.

Gradually the officina (the room in the pharmacy open to the public and also serving for the preparation of medicines) became filled with increasing numbers of decorative wooden, glass, majolica, and porcelain vessels, bronze mortars and pestles of all sizes and elaborate ornamentation, as well as other instruments necessary for the preparation of medicines. Nowadays these items are prized ornamental antiques and they have captivated many a collector. Study of the furnishings and equipment of old-time pharmacies, however, is also useful as a means of learning about the medicines used in those days, in this instance mainly drugs.

It was not until the development of organic chemistry, launched in 1805 by the pharmacist Friedrich Wilhelm Sertürner (1783—1841) when he isolated the opium alkaloid morphine, that the ground was laid for the development of pharmaceutical chemistry. With the late 19th and early 20th century came the widespread production of synthetic medicines. With this 'victory over nature' there was a rapid swing away from the use of medicinal plants in therapy.

It seemed that the traditions of thousands of years would not save medicinal plants from falling into disuse. However the opposite proved to be the case when it was discovered that though they have many advantages, synthetic medicines also frequently have their drawbacks in the form of unpleasant side-effects. The synthetic medicines that were produced over the years far outnumbered the two to three hundred species of medicinal plants but how many of them lasted any length of time? Perhaps only acetylsalicylic acid

17th century wood veneer vessel for extract of licorice.

17th century glass apothecary vessel from the Thuringian glassworks (a). The inscription denotes that the vessel contains (or rather is intended to contain) a tincture of *Asa foetida*.

Italian-style majolica apothecary vessel made in northern Holland in the late 16th century (b).

a

b

(aspirin) has survived with all its well-deserved reputation to this day. It is, however, only a semi-synthetic version of the natural salicylic acid isolated from an old well-known drug obtained from willow bark, that was once used to treat fever in diseases associated with chilling. What praises were heaped in their day on barbiturates, amidopyrin, and phenacetin and now all medicines containing these substances are being eliminated from therapy because of their unfavourable effect on the human organism. This example alone is enough to refute the claims of certain advocates of chemotherapy as to the exclusive standing of synthetic medicines.

Currently medicines are classed as either 'hard' or 'soft'. The first group includes synthetic medicines, the second most drugs from medicinal plants and naturally also preparations from these drugs such as herbal teas, infusions, tinctures and extracts. The objective person must acknowledge that we need both groups of medicines.

Synthetic medicines enable the physician to give rapid and effective treatment in acute cases. Natural medicines, on the other hand, if administered correctly, generally have a mild action and the effect usually occurs after a lengthier period. They serve to protect against infectious diseases, are good for treating chronic diseases, contribute to the patient's progress in convalescence, have a calming effect mainly in the case of elderly patients, and are also of great importance in pediatrics because of their relative safety if used responsibly. However not all medicinal plants have a mild action. Their number also includes species that have a rapid effect and are ***extremely poisonous even in small doses.*** Examples are ***Deadly Nightshade, Autumn Crocus,*** and ***Lily of the valley.*** Besides these there are some medicinal plants that are ***potentially poisonous and therefore dangerous if used for self-medication by the layman*** e. g. ***Arnica*** and ***Greater Celandine.*** Nevertheless there are still many plants that have a mild but definite therapeutic effect and can prove useful as home remedies. It is mainly these that are dealt with in this book. It must be stressed, however, that you should not hesitate to seek professional medical advice

11

quickly, should the herbal remedies not prove effective within a reasonable length of time and immediately if the condition worsens.

Just as chemistry has untold possibilities of coming up with new and effective synthetic medicines, so phytotherapy has opportunities of discovering new natural medicines in the plant realm. Chemotherapy and phytotherapy are both effective if treatment is properly selected, and the two can also be successfully combined.

To date man has discovered only about 10 per cent of the many and diverse existing plant species and thus the prospects of research in the field of natural medicines are bright indeed. Antibiotics, hormones, vitamins, prostaglandines — all have their origin and basis in nature. New methods of plant tissue culture and biotechnology are beginning to point the way towards producing valuable natural substances in the test tube. There are even hopeful signs that man may discover further natural medicines to combat cancer and diseases caused by the process of aging.

THE MAIN GROUPS OF ACTIVE PRINCIPLES OR CONSTITUENTS OBTAINED FROM MEDICINAL PLANTS

The medicinal action of some species of plants is determined by their constituents. These affect the condition and function of the various organs in the human body, clear up residual symptoms or destroy the cause of the disease — in most cases infectious micro-organisms. They help increase the body's resistance to disease, retard or ease the processes of natural aging or facilitate the adaptation of the organism to certain conditions.

Over the centuries man made use of medicinal plants even though he was unable to find a rational explanation for their effects. It was not until the 19th century and the rapid development of organic chemistry and pharmacology, that man determined which active principles or group of principles are responsible for a given therapeutic effect. Knowledge of these substances made possible not only their application in therapy but natural substances frequently served as a model for the synthetic preparation of new medicines, enabling the drug to be modified and made more effective. It was soon discovered that a better therapeutic effect was often obtained by the particular combination of active principles naturally present in each plant than by a single, isolated substance. The outcome of this is that there has been a marked renewal of medical interest in classic phytotherapy.

The following text will acquaint the reader with the basic groups of active principles that are useful in the treatment of disease. The principal constituents of each of the illustrated species in this book are included in the accompanying description. The most important active constituents are the alkaloids, glycosides, essential oils, tannins and bitter principles — products of secondary metabolism in plants. Also important are the products of primary metabolism in plants, mainly sugars, fatty oils, and organic acids. Besides these all plants contain further components (amino acids, enzymes, peptides, vitamins, etc.) which themselves have no therapeutic effect but may possibly increase the efficiency of the therapeutically important principles.

Alkaloids

Alkaloids rank among the most efficient and therapeutically significant plant substances. They are a chemically very diverse group of organic nitrogen compounds. *Generally they are extremely toxic* though they do have a marked therapeutic effect in minute quantities. For this reason plants containing alkaloids were not often used in folk medicine and then for external application only. Pure, isolated plant alkaloids and their synthetic derivatives are used as basic medicinal agents all over the world for their analgesic, antispasmodic, and bactericidal effects. Examples of such alkaloidal plants mentioned in this book are *Greater Celandine, Autumn Crocus, Jimsonweed* and *White Hellebore.* The number of isolated alkaloids, however, already totals several thousand, though only several hundred are used in therapy. In recent years attention has been focused on alkaloids with anti-tumourous effects. *These plants must never be self-administered.*

Glycosides

Glycosides are complex organic substances that when hydrolysed (split by the action of water, acids or enzymes) separate into two parts — a sugar (glycone) component and nonsugar (aglycone) component. *Some glycosides often have a pronounced physiological action and are poisonous to man.* These include, for instance, the cardiac glycosides affecting the muscle tissue of the heart found in *Foxglove* (without which treatment of heart diseases is quite unthinkable nowadays), and the glycosides found in *Adonis* and *Lily of the valley.* Used in therapy are glycosides with a laxative action (Alder Buckthorn, Medicinal Rhubarb), an anti-inflammatory effect (Agrimony, Pot Marigold, Scented Mayweed), diuretic and antiseptic properties, etc. Flavonoids, flavonolignans and coumarin derivatives have an important effect on inflammatory processes, liver and gall bladder diseases, some circulatory disorders, and the like (St. John's Wort, Agrimony, Milk Thistle, Buckwheat). Glycosides also include saponins, a striking physiological characteristic of which is that they produce a soapy foam. The expectorant action is extremely useful in reducing inflammation of the upper respiratory passages. *As alkaloids, glycosides must never be self-administered.*

Essential oils

Essential oils are generally aromatic, volatile, organic compounds of 'oil-like character'. They contain terpenes, sesquiterpenes and other components and have a wide range of therapeutic uses. Essential oils extracted from Wild Thyme and Garden Thyme are used internally for treating infections of the upper respiratory passages, while extracts of Yarrow, Sweet-Flag, Angelica and Fennel are used in respect of infections of the digestive tract. Similarly, infections of the kidneys, bladder and urinary tract are treated with essential oils of Juniper and Parsley. Also put to good use are the reddening and desensitizing effects of essential oils in the treatment of inflammation of the muscles and tendons and rheumatism in the form of various liniments that relieve pain such as Rosemary and Peppermint. Some essential oils are the principal components of various flavouring agents that also have a favourable effect on digestion, for example Dill, Caraway, Anise, and Fennel. They stimulate the appetite, promote the flow of gastric secretions and bile, and relieve flatulence. Essential oils also play an important part in medicinal and natural cosmetics.

Tannins

Tannins are organic substances of diverse composition with pronounced astringent properties that hasten the healing of wounds and inflamed mucous membranes. Externally, the bark of Oak, Lady's Mantle, Agrimony and Garden Sage, are used for treating varicose ulcers, haemorrhoids, frost-bites and burns, as mouthwashes for treating inflammation and periodontal disease. Internally they are used to treat diarrhoea and biliousness.

Bitter principles

Bitter principles are organic substances of extremely varied chemical composition. In therapeutic doses they stimulate the flow of gastric secretions and help improve digestion. The effect of stomach bitters and various aperitifs such as vermouths is based on the content of bitter principles in these drinks, the same as in stomachic drops made from Centaury, Wormwood or Blessed Thistle.

This brings us to the end of the group of active constituents that are the so-called secondary metabolites of plants and which are responsible for the plant's therapeutic effect. Of greater importance for plants themselves, of course, are the products of primary metabolism which are necessary for the proper function of the basic life processes in plants. They are also of use to man. This group includes sugars, fatty oils, and organic acids.

Sugars

Sugars of all compositions are an inseparable part of many medicinal preparations. Glucose is a component of invigorating nourishing preparations, fructose is important for the diet of diabetics, and there are many who would not dispute the healing properties of honey. Dextrans are complex sugars obtained from glucose by the action of certain micro-organisms and are used in solutions as a substitute for blood plasma. Mucilages, important components of medicines for treating inflammation of the upper respiratory passages and intestines, are also complex sugars and are extracted from Coltsfoot, Mallow, Ribwort, and Mullein.

Fatty oils

Fatty oils in plants serve as a store of energy. They are compounds of glycerol and fatty acids. Isolated they are used in ointments, medicines and cosmetics and also play an important part in the treatment of diseases of the digestive system.

Organic acids

Organic acids are a further group of products of primary metabolism in plants. Biogenetically they are close to sugars and are found in all plants. The most familiar are malic acid, citric acid, and tartaric acid.

Even this very simplified breakdown of important substances clearly shows their chemical diversity and wide range of uses.

COLLECTION OF MEDICINAL PLANTS

Medicinal plants are obtained either by collecting in the wild or by cultivation. Both methods have a tradition of long standing. Medicinal plants were collected in ancient times by so-called rhizotomes who also dried and sold them to healers. Even in the Middle Ages there were professional herb collectors. Mention of this may be found in the 12th century German manuscript of Apuleius-Dioscorides in which herb collecting is realistically depicted by one of the illuminations.

The tradition of cultivating medicinal plants can be traced back to the monastery gardens of the Benedictine monks. Later they were also cultivated by other orders. In time they were to be found in castle gardens and gardens adjoining pharmacies, then in the gardens of peasants and finally in fields.

Even in modern times man cannot get along without the collection and cultivation of medicinal plants, though in future years cultivation will probably take over because of the advantages of the concentration of crops.

To obtain drugs from medicinal plants they must be processed according to specific rules in order that they retain their required therapeutic value.

Before dealing with the individual rules it is necessary to explain the relationship between medicinal plant and drug. A medicinal plant, growing wild or cultivated, contains therapeutically active substances suitable for treating diseases. The active constituents are found to be present in greater concentrations in certain parts of the plant. Such parts are collected and preserved by the simplest method, that is drying. The dried plant parts—top, leaves, flowers, fruits, and rootstock—are called *drugs* in pharmaceutical language. Such drugs have nothing in common with the addictive narcotic drugs that are often the subject of abuse and criminal activity. The latter meaning for the word 'drug' probably stems from the fact that the first addictive substances came from drugs that were also used for medicinal purposes, for instance, opium, certain of its alkaloids and their derivatives, the leaves of coca and the cocaine isolated from them, etc. Here however, the term 'drug' has only the one meaning—that of an original, simple, medicinal substance.

15

TEN RULES FOR COLLECTING MEDICINAL PLANTS

1. The first requirement for correct collection is a good knowledge of the medicinal plants you want to collect. You mustn't just *think* you are gathering a certain species — *you must know exactly.* This book aims to aid identification by illustrating a number of plants. *Mistaken identification may sometimes be fatal if the respective plant is poisonous. Therefore it is absolutely essential that a plant has been correctly identified before administering. If in any doubt, seek professional advice.*

2. *Poisonous and dangerous plants and ones that they resemble and for which they may readily be mistaken should not be gathered by children.*

3. If you wish to sell the plants you gather then you cannot collect several different species of medicinal plants at the same time with good results. It is better to specialize. This brings with it irreplaceable practical experience, which results in a drug of top quality. Before collecting medicinal plants for sale you should make specific arrangements with the buyer.

4. When collecting medicinal plants in the wild you must never gather all the specimens of the respective species in a given locality but must remember to leave enough to ensure its continued survival in the area. There are many known instances where indiscriminate collecting almost resulted in the total extinction of a species in a particular area. Gentians, which were formerly relatively abundant, must now be rigidly protected so they do not become extinct. Their decline was caused by collectors supported primarily by producers of stomach bitters. The once plentiful Buckbean, Sundew, Arnica and other plants have also similarly declined. It is the obligation of every person who collects medicinal plants to take an active part in protecting nature! When gathering lime-tree blossoms or birch leaves, for example, one cannot cut off whole branches just to make collecting them easier and quicker!

5. When gathering medicinal plants it is best to wear gloves and to use tools such as secateurs, knives, sickles with a honed edge, special digging implements, and the like, which you will probably have adapted to your own needs. They facilitate collecting and make it possible to obtain crude drugs of better quality.

6. Select the proper receptacle for the parts of the plants you will be collecting. For instance, flowers and soft leaves should be put loosely in a basket — they shouldn't be packed tightly as they may become overheated and 'sweat' during transport. Hardier plant parts, such as rhizomes, roots and stiff top parts, may be put in carryalls or sacks. In the case of large quantities you can use pallets which can be stacked. During handling and transport any plant parts you have collected should be arranged loosely and treated with care to prevent accidental damage, otherwise they may begin to ferment.

7. Gather only healthy, visibly undamaged plants. Do not collect plants that are diseased or infested with pests. Do not collect plants that are spattered with mud or covered with dust or plants growing alongside thoroughfares and much-frequented roads and paths. In such places there is danger of the undesirable concentration of heavy metals, such as lead in the plants.

8. Do not gather medicinal plants in grasslands or orchards where weed-killers and pesticides have been used, i.e. agents used to protect cultivated plants against disease, pests and weeds. Also avoid places that are suspected of having been treated with such preparations. There are two main reasons for this. Pesticides have a prescribed period of effectiveness and until the time of its expiry plants sprayed with these agents are poisonous. Some preparations do not remain only on the surface of the leaves, etc. but are metabolized by the plant and their residues, which are usually harmful, become entrenched in some of the active constituents, for example, essential oil.

9. Plants should not be gathered when they are wet with dew or rain or in the cool of the evening when dampness falls. Such damp plant parts rapidly spoil from overheating and the condensation of moisture. They soon begin to ferment and the concurrent biochemical processes in the wilting plant parts affect not only their appearance—browning and darkening in colour—but also the active constituents, which begin to break down or at the very least their concentration decreases. In general the best time for collecting medicinal plants is in dry sunny weather between ten in the morning and five in the afternoon.

10. The collected plant parts should be dried as soon as possible after harvesting and, after being allowed to air for a while, put in suitable containers, as a rule paper bags, closed tins or stoppered glass jars. Drugs must be stored in a dry, dark place and at a relatively low temperature, not exceeding 15 °C, in airtight containers that help prevent their deterioration and contamination.

PROPER DRYING OF MEDICINAL PLANTS—
A NECESSITY FOR THE DRUG'S EFFICACY

The collected plant parts should be transported to the place where they are to be dried as quickly as possible—that is the first condition for obtaining a good-quality drug. Medicinal plants cultivated as large-scale crops are dried in industrial drying sheds where the temperature can be regulated. When drying plants at home it is necessary to adapt conditions as well as possible.

At home the materials should be dried in airy, dry and well-ventilated premises, on flat, rust-free steel-meshed or firm fabric-meshed frames. They may also be dried on clean paper, on a sheet, or even on a clean wooden floor. There is no need to stress the necessity for hygiene in drying. It is also very important that the plants be spread out in thin layers to dry in order to prevent spoilage by overheating and moisture condensation as well as uneven drying. As far as possible the plant material should be dried without being turned, nor should it be handled unnecessarily, in order to prevent needless crumbling and a poor appearance of the end product. The best quality drugs are obtained by natural drying coupled with good air circulation. Occasionally, however, there is no way to avoid drying at a higher temperature or to complete drying by artificial means. In such instances you should see that the temperature does not exceed 40 °C. This is particularly important in the case of plants containing essential oils that easily evaporate. It is preferable to dry in shade. Only the flowers of Mullein may very occasionally be dried in bright sunlight. Drying time depends on the plant's water content and on the temperature at which drying takes place. Leaves and flowers dry quickest, followed by the top parts of the plant. Roots, rhizomes, tubers and fleshy fruits take the longest to dry.

Drying must be as rapid as possible. If the plant parts break easily when bent then they are sufficiently dry. The appearance of the end product is an indication of whether the plant material has been properly dried or not. As far as possible it should retain the colour of the living plant, perhaps only with a slight difference in the shade due to loss of water. This means, for example, that the flowerheads of Scented Mayweed must have a golden-yellow centre, white ligulate flowers, and must not disintegrate, that the flowers of Mullein must remain a deep yellow, and the flowers of Deadnettle creamy-white. Leaves must retain their green coloration and in the case of rootstock there must be no pronounced darkening in colour nor change in aroma.

During the drying process the plant parts lose water and consequently a proportion of their weight. An important economic statistic is the drying ratio. This depends on the plant part being dried and on the conditions in which the plant grew. Bark, seeds and dry fruits lose practically no water at all and have the lowest drying ratio, whereas fleshy fruits such as elderberries and bilberries have a drying ratio of 8 to 10:1. The drying ratio of flowers is 6 to 8:1. Knowing the drying ratio is an important technical as well as economic statistic for those who collect as well as those who cultivate medicinal plants.

Crude drugs are stored either whole or crumbled. Most dried flowers, fruits and seeds are not crumbled. Dried leaves and top parts are cut up, dried roots are crushed or ground. Thick, fleshy roots are peeled and cubed or sliced into rounds before drying. In large-scale commercial operations industrial cutting machines, grinding mills, sieves, separators and presses are used for this purpose. Medicinal plants that have been dried are sold in crude drug form—without further preparation. This the plant collector may do only for the purpose of his own, home use.

The text accompanying each of the plants in this book tells how to prepare the respective crude drug prior to making the medicinal infusion as well as how to improve the steeping process and make the drug more effective. The drug should be prepared (crushed or crumbled) just before use. A drug loses its potency more rapidly when stored in the crumbled state. The active principles are also affected by periodic absorption of moisture and drying out as well as by extremes of temperature.

STORING DRUGS

A question often asked is how long will drugs remain sufficiently potent. Experience has shown that long-term storage lowers a drug's potency because many of its active principles gradually break down. It is recommended not to use drugs more than two years old and for home use preferably to replace them yearly.

Proper storage is important to preserve the quality of a drug. The general rule is the same as for most natural material: always keep drugs in dry, cool and dark conditions. As for containers, large amounts can be stored in paper multiwall-bags, burlap sacks, cartons, drums, metal containers, etc. Plastic containers should not be used. Stored drugs should be checked regularly, at least once a month. Like all vegetable material and foodstuffs they may be attacked by storehouse pests. In such a case the respective drug should be discarded.

Careful attention should also be paid to labelling! Never rely on remembering where a given drug is or what container it is stored in. The label should include the year it was harvested.

Containers with poisonous drugs must be clearly marked with the symbol ☠ so there won't be any danger of their being mistaken for some other drug therefore resulting in accidental poisoning.

PREPARATION OF HERBAL TEAS FOR HOME REMEDIES

The dosages given in this book are those generally used in practice.

Teaspoon — a full (not heaping) teaspoon is the equivalent of about 2 g of herbal tea mixture, 1.5 g of dried flowers, and 3 g of dried roots or fruits.

Tablespoon — a full tablespoon is the equivalent of about 5 g of herbal tea mixture, 4 g of dried flowers or leaves, and 7 g of dried roots or fruits.

A cup is the equivalent of about 125 ml.

A glass is the equivalent of about 200 ml.

For home remedies drugs are usually administered in the form of infusions—short-term infusions, long-term infusions or decoctions. To prepare them always use porcelain or glass vessels and lids of the same material or else enamelled lids.

Short-term infusion (infusum) is the commonest method of preparing medicinal teas. Boiling water is poured over the crushed or crumbled drug, covered with a lid and left to steep in a warm place for at least ten to fifteen minutes. This is then poured through a thick-meshed plastic strainer and sipped slowly.

Long-term infusion (maceratio) is the method used for preparing those drugs whose active constituents break down when boiled. Warm water (15 to 20 °C) is poured over the crumbled drug, covered with a lid and left to steep, best of all overnight when it is to be taken in the morning and throughout the day when it is to be taken at bedtime. Before drinking it the infusion should be stirred thoroughly and then strained. It should be sipped slowly. This method is recommended mainly for mucilaginous drugs.

Decoction (decoctum) is the method of extracting the soluble principles from a drug by boiling. The crumbled drug is boiled for five to ten minutes in a covered flame-proof glass, enamel or stainless steel dish. It is then removed from the heat and left to stand until it is cool enough to drink, after which it is strained and sipped slowly or taken by the spoonful.

Tinctures and extracts are best purchased at the pharmacy where they are prepared correctly and professionally. *Tinctures* are prepared by steeping the crude drug in alcohol using a special apparatus. *Extracts* are obtained by treating the drug with water, alcohol or ether and have a thicker consistency than tinctures. They are divided according to their consistency as follows: fluid or liquid extracts (*extracta fluida*) containing more than 20 percent water, thin or soft extracts (*extracta tenua*) containing 10 to 20 percent water, and thick or solid extracts (*extracta spissa*) containing less than 10 percent water. Dry extracts (*extracta sicca, pulverisata*) are extracts that are almost completely evaporated and pulverized—like a powder.

Natural plant juices (*succus*) are juices obtained by crushing and pressing fresh plants or plant parts. These are crumbled in a non-metal vessel and pressed through a clean cloth. The juice is used as is or else carefully evaporated in part and thickened with sugar. Juices have the disadvantage that they do not keep well and can be obtained only at a certain time of the year. Nowadays the pharmaceutical industry processes juices that do not keep well into more lasting forms, thereby facilitating their long-term use.

SIDE-EFFECTS OF MEDICINAL PLANTS

When taken in the right dosage, drugs rarely have unpleasant side-effects. These may, however, occur where a plant contains a substance which has a more pronounced effect if used over a long period without a break, or in excessive doses. This happens, for instance, when treating heart diseases with *digitalis glycosides*. Long-term use leads to their accumulation in the heart muscle and to their sudden toxic action. *The medicine suddenly becomes a poison.* Therefore, it is not recommended that this plant be used in self-treatment. Long-term use of *Juniper* has an adverse effect on the kidneys. Long intensive use of *Wormwood* causes dementia. Uninterrupted continuous drinking of *mint tea* has an adverse effect on the blood count. Uninterrupted continuous use of plant laxative may become a habit and lead to the disruption of natural elimination. Recent years have also seen a marked increase in allergic reactions to *Scented Mayweed*, most often in its external use in cosmetics. Allergic reactions and skin damage are also known in the case of *Rue, Bishop's Weed*, which furthermore carries with it the danger of liver and kidney damage, and *Blessed Thistle*. A further unpleasant side-effect of medicinal plants is the disease known as fagopyrism or hypericism caused by the use of *Buckwheat* or *St. John's Wort*. The disease manifests itself only in the case of simultaneous exposure to the sun in the form of skin damage or even tissue mortification. From the several aforesaid examples it is obvious that medicinal plants and drugs from natural substances can be highly dangerous or even lethal if they are not administered in suitable doses and for the prescribed period or length of time. Paracelsus' classic saying that 'all substances are poison and nothing is without a poisonous effect, that only the dosage determines whether what we take is poisonous or not', holds true for medicinal plants and their extracts as well.

Table of illustrated medicinal plants and the main disorders for the treatment of which their various parts are used

Medicinal plant	Diseases of the digestive system	Diseases of the kidneys and urinary tract	Diseases of the heart and vascular system	Diseases of the nervous system	Diseases of the respiratory tract	External wounds and dermatitis
Achillea millefolium	flowering stems, flowers					flowering stems, inflorescence
Acorus calamus	rhizome					rhizome
Adonis vernalis			top parts			
Aesculus hippocastanum			fruits			
Agrimonia eupatoria	flowering stems					flowering stems
Agropyron repens		rhizome				
Alcea rosea					flowers	
Alchemilla xanthochlora	flowering stems, leaves	flowering stems, leaves				flowering stems, leaves
Althaea officinalis	rootstock, leaves				rootstock, leaves	leaves
Anethum graveolens	fruit, top parts					
Angelica archangelica	rhizome			rhizome		
Arctium lappa	rootstock	rootstock				rootstock
Arctostaphylos uva-ursi		leaves				
Arnica montana			flowers			flowers
Artemisia absinthium	flowering stems			flowering stems		
Betula pendula		leaves				leaves

Medicinal plant	Diseases of the digestive system	Diseases of the kidneys and urinary tract	Diseases of the heart and vascular system	Diseases of the nervous system	Diseases of the respiratory tract	External wounds and dermatitis
Borago officinalis		flowering stems		flowering stems		
Calendula officinalis	flowers					flowers
Capsella bursa-pastoris		flowering stems				flowering stems
Carum carvi	fruits					
Centaurium erythraea	flowering stems					
Cetraria islandica				thallus		
Chamaemelum nobile	flowers					flowers
Chamomilla recutita	flowers					flowers
Chelidonium majus	flowering stems					flowering stems
Cichorium intybus	rootstock					
Cnicus benedictus	flowering stems					
Colchicum autumnale	gout and cancer—fruit, seeds					
Convallaria majalis			leaves, flowering stems			
Coriandrum sativum	fruits			fruits		fruits
Crataegus laevigata			flowers, flowers and leaves, fruit			
Cynara scolymus	leaves					
Datura stramonium				leaves, seeds	leaves, seeds	

Medicinal plant	Diseases of the digestive system	Diseases of the kidneys and urinary tract	Diseases of the heart and vascular system	Diseases of the nervous system	Diseases of the respiratory tract	External wounds and dermatitis
Drosera rotundifolia			entire plant	entire plant	entire plant	
Dryopteris filix-mas	for eliminating intestinal worms—rhizome					
Equisetum arvense		entire plant			entire plant	
Euphrasia rostkoviana	eye diseases—flowering stems					
Fagopyrum esculentum	diseases caused by venous insufficiency—flowering stems					
Foeniculum vulgare	fruit				fruit	
Fragaria vesca	leaves	leaves				leaves
Galeopsis segetum					flowering stems	
Galium odoratum		flowering stems		flowering stems		
Glycyrrhiza glabra	rootstock					
Herniaria glabra		flowering stems				
Hippophaë rhamnoides	vitamin drug				fruits	
Humulus lupulus				fruits		
Hypericum perforatum	flowering stems			flowering stems		
Inula helenium					rhizome	
Juniperus communis	fruit	fruit				
Lamium album		flowers		flowers		flowers

Medicinal plant	Diseases of the digestive system	Diseases of the kidneys and urinary tract	Diseases of the heart and vascular system	Diseases of the nervous system	Diseases of the respiratory tract	External wounds and dermatitis
Lavandula angustifolia	flowers, flowering stems			flowers, flowering stems		
Leonurus cardiaca		flowering stems	flowering stems	flowering stems		
Levisticum officinale	rhizome	rhizome				
Linaria vulgaris	flowering stems	flowering stems				flowering stems
Marrubium vulgare	flowering stems			flowering stems		
Melissa officinalis	flowering stems			flowering stems		
Mentha × *piperita*	leaves, flowering stems					
Menyanthes trifoliata	leaves					
Ocimum basilicum	flowering stems					
Ononis spinosa		rhizomes				
Origanum vulgare	flowering stems					
Petroselinum crispum		rootstock, fruit				
Pimpinella anisum	fruit	fruit			fruit	
Pimpinella saxifraga		rootstock			rootstock	rootstock
Plantago lanceolata					leaves	leaves
Polygonum hydropiper		flowering stems			flowering stems	flowering stems
Potentilla anserina	flowering stems					flowering stems

Medicinal plant	Diseases of the digestive system	Diseases of the kidneys and urinary tract	Diseases of the heart and vascular system	Diseases of the nervous system	Diseases of the respiratory tract	External wounds and dermatitis
Primula elatior					flowering stems	
Prunus spinosa	flowers, fruit	flowers, fruit				
Pulmonaria officinalis					flowering stems	flowering stems
Quercus robur						bark
Rhamnus frangula	bark					
Ribes nigrum	leaves, fruit	leaves			leaves	
Rosa canina	vitamin drug				fruit	
Rosmarinus officinalis	leaves		leaves	leaves		leaves
Rubia tinctorum		rootstock				
Ruta graveolens	nonflowering stems			nonflowering stems		
Salvia officinalis	flowering stems, leaves				flowering stems, leaves	flowering stems, leaves
Sambucus nigra		flowers, fruits			flowers, fruits	
Silybum marianum	fruit					
Symphytum officinale						rootstock
Taraxacum officinale	rootstock, flowers and leaves	rootstock, flowers and leaves				
Thymus serpyllum	flowering stems				flowering stems	
Thymus vulgaris	flowering stems				flowering stems	

Medicinal plant	Diseases of the digestive system	Diseases of the kidneys and urinary tract	Diseases of the heart and vascular system	Diseases of the nervous system	Diseases of the respiratory tract	External wounds and dermatitis
Tilia cordata		flowers			flowers	
Trigonella foenum-grae-cum						seeds
Tropaeolum majus		seeds			seeds	
Tussilago farfara					flowers, leaves	flowers, leaves
Urtica dioica		flowering stems, leaves				
Vaccinium myrtillus	fruit	leaves				leaves, fruit
Valeriana officinalis			rootstock	rootstock		
Veratrum album	antineuralgic effect of rhizome					
Verbascum densiflorum		flowers			flowers	flowers
Verbena officinalis	flowering stems	flowering stems				flowering stems
Viola tricolor		flowering stems			flowering stems	flowering stems
Viscum album			flowering stems			

COLOR PLATES

NOTE:

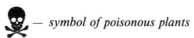 — *symbol of poisonous plants*

Yarrow, Milfoil
Achillea millefolium L.

Compositae

Of more than one hundred species belonging to this genus, Yarrow is the most widely used medicinally. This is because it is commonly distributed throughout the temperate zone of Europe and Asia and is readily obtainable. Closely related species are also collected for the drug market. Yarrow is likewise present in North America, Australia and New Zealand, where it was introduced. The flowering stems and sometimes only the flowers are collected for medicinal use. This must not include the leafless and woody lower sections of the stem and the flowers must not be past their prime. They should be dried carefully in a shaded spot. The drug has a pleasant aromatic odour and slightly bitter taste. The principal constituent is an essential oil which has an anti-inflammatory action; other constituents include bitter principles and to a limited degree also tannins. It is administered internally in the form of an infusion (one tablespoon of the drug to one cup boiling water) in nonspecific digestive upsets, including gall bladder complaints. In the case of weakened gastric function it acts as an aromatic bitter principle stimulating the appetite. Also important is the age-old use of Yarrow in the treatment of gynaecological disorders, for example painful spasms of the uterine ligaments, and menstrual pains. Externally the antiseptic properties of the infusion are used in the form of compresses and baths to treat ulcers, slow-healing wounds and skin rashes. If administered in greater doses than the usual innocuous ones, Yarrow may cause undesirable reactions such as faintness, or skin irritation. Its clotting effects, dating mainly from the days of medieval healing, are negligible. Yarrow's generally acknowledged therapeutic properties are the reason for its inclusion in pharmacopoeias and pharmaceutical compendiums.

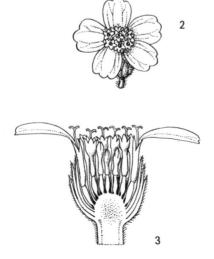

2

3

Yarrow (1) is a typical, relatively common plant of sunny banks, field boundaries and pastures, from lowland to mountain elevations. The small flowerheads (2), arranged in flat corymbose panicles, indicate that the plant is a member of the Compositae family. The longitudinal section of the flowerhead (3), shows the arrangement of tubular florets in the centre surrounded by strap-shaped florets on the margin. The corolla is generally

coloured white, but pink flowers (4) are
not uncommon. This variability of
coloration in no way affects the drug's
effectiveness, and so pink-flowering
Yarrow may likewise be collected for
medicinal use. The flowering period is
from June until September. The fruits
are long, silvery-grey achenes (cypselas)
with narrow wings on either side.
Smaller Yarrows with sulphur or bright
yellow flowers are often to be found in
rock gardens.

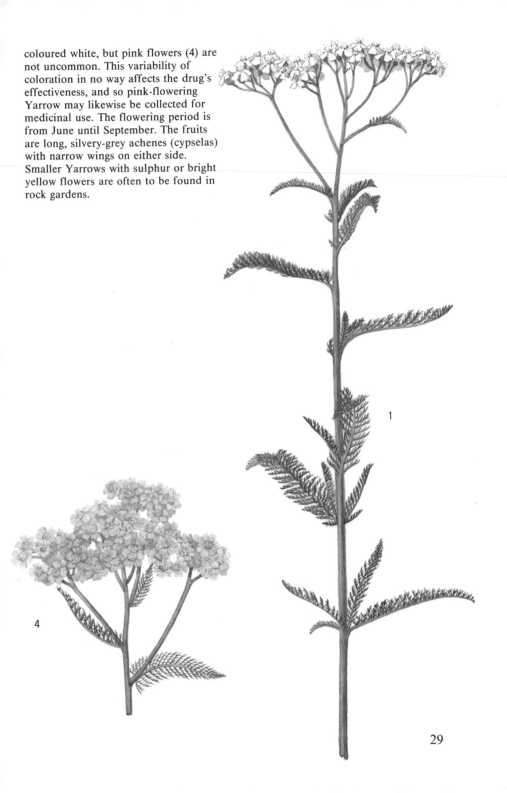

1

4

29

Sweet Flag
Acorus calamus L.

Sweet Flag is a plant of the northern hemisphere. There are several types, each differing in the number of chromosomes but otherwise practically identical in appearance. Besides the normal diploid race found in North America there are those with three times and even four times the basic, monoploid chromosome number. Sweet Flag is native to southern Asia whence it was apparently brought to Europe via the Balkans by Turks, Tatars, and perhaps even Crusaders. As early as the 17th century it was already a popular medicinal as well as culinary herb. It grows beside shallow, slow-flowing waterways and multiplies only by vegetative means. Plants growing in Europe are sterile. The rhizome contains an aromatic essential oil, tannins and bitter principles and it is these constituents that have a medicinal effect. Sweet Flag is used to treat digestive disorders and loss of appetite, particularly if these are of nervous origin. The dried rhizome is prepared in the form of an infusion and may also be boiled briefly. It is also used in powder form and as an alcohol extract. One teaspoonful of the crushed drug per one cup boiling water is sufficient for the infusion. The dosage for the powder is the amount taken up by the tip of a knife. The tincture is taken by drops, a single dose equalling twenty drops. The drug in its various forms is taken three to four times daily before meals. The alcohol extract is also used externally as a rub to alleviate tired and sore muscles and as a stimulating agent in baths. Sweet Flag is used to make stomachic liqueurs and has been popular since ancient times in India, Egypt and Greece.

The most striking characteristic of Sweet Flag (1) is the thick, pleasantly aromatic rhizome with leaves up to one metre long growing from the upper side and countless wiry roots below. The flowerhead is a spadix (2), ten to twenty

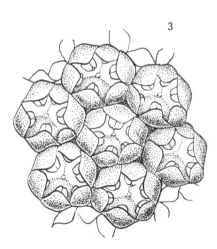

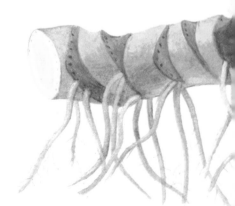

30

cm long, with flowers opening from the base upward and arranged in an unusual architectural pattern (3). The flowers are minute with six perianth segments and six stamens in two rings of three each. The fruits, practically unknown in Europe, are red, many-seeded berries. Besides Sweet Flag only one other species of *Acorus* has

been described to date — *Acorus gramineus* Soland., native to the Far East. It is a miniature plant grown in several ornamental forms in aquariums.

2

1

Yellow Pheasant's Eye, Spring Adonis
Adonis vernalis L.

Ranunculaceae

Yellow Pheasant's Eye is one of the loveliest of the spring flowers growing in Europe. Nowadays it is found only rarely in the remains of steppe localities. Its native habitat extends from the spreading Russian steppes located in the temperate zone, roughly along latitude 50 ° N as far as western Siberia and the foothills of the Altai Mountains. It was the Russian school of medicine that first came forward with information about its therapeutic uses, mainly its reliable sedative effects in the treatment of various types of cardiac neuroses. The carefully dried top parts are used in commercially manufactured drugs and are collected in spring at the beginning of the flowering period. Both flowering and non-flowering stems are gathered. Cardiac glycosides present in the drug are responsible not only for its medicinal effect but also for the plant's poisonous properties. It is for this reason that the drug and preparations made from it are dispensed only on prescription by a physician and administered only under his supervision. It is used in the form of an infusion, alcohol extract (tincture or extract), or pharmaceutical specialty-type preparations, mainly in the treatment of cardiac neurosis manifesting itself by a more rapid pulse rate or premature contractions of the heart muscle. It is also used with success in the treatment of certain types of myocarditis, cardiac insufficiency in the elderly, and low blood pressure, being noted for its rapid but short-term effect. The drug's diuretic properties ensure that the cardiac glycosides do not accumulate in the patient's body and do not cause toxic symptoms, if used correctly. Pheasant's Eye continues to be an important drug in current pharmacopoeias and its effective substances are to be found in a number of commercial pharmaceutical preparations.

Yellow Pheasant's Eye (1) is a perennial herb, twenty to forty centimetres high, bearing striking, large, shiny, golden-yellow radiate flowers in spring as early as the end of April. After they are spent they form an aggregate fruit (2) composed of nearly globose achenes with a hooked beak. The green, seemingly unripe aggregate fruit breaks up rapidly into its individual parts and the achenes collected at this time are the ones best suited for sowing. This is well known to rock garden specialists who practise the propagation of Pheasant's Eye by seed. The less striking annual species of *Adonis* occasionally grow wild in Europe's fields. They contain

32

glycosides similar to those present in Yellow Pheasant's Eye, but in negligible amounts and for that reason, apart from a few exceptions, are not used medicinally. Most familiar is Summer Pheasant's Eye (*Adonis aestivalis*) (3) which has red flowers.

WARNING: This herb is poisonous even in very small amounts and must be used only by registered medical practitioners.

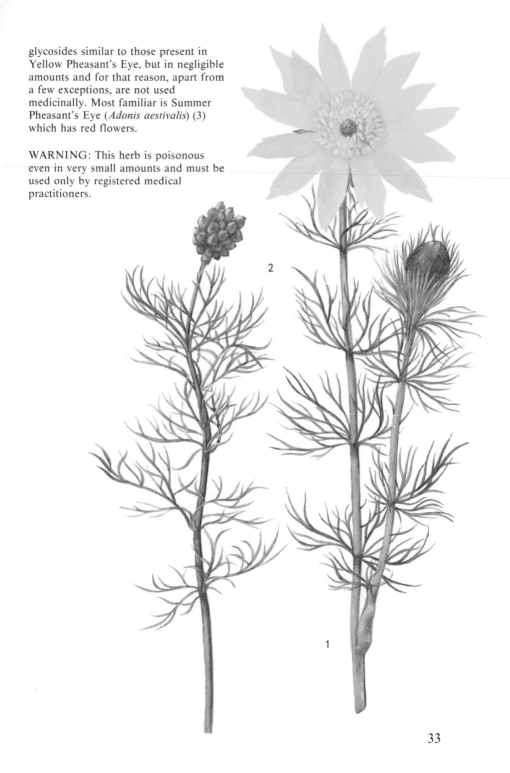

Horse Chestnut
Aesculus hippocastanum L.
Hippocastanaceae

This tree, introduced into Europe and cultivated there since the 16th century, is indigenous to certain hills of the Balkan Peninsula, where this remarkable tertiary relict still grows wild. Its most closely related species are found in the Himalayas, East Asia and North America. Chiefly used for medicinal purposes are the seeds—ripe Horse Chestnuts or conkers, which are processed by the pharmaceutical industry. They contain saponins, of which aescin is the most important, and also flavonoid glycosides. The drug is used mainly for the treatment of vascular diseases, generally designated as vascular insufficiency, which includes the treatment of varicose veins, varicose ulcers and haemorrhoids. Aescin and its ancillary substances have a beneficial effect on the capillaries in that they act as vasodilators. They also improve the elasticity of the blood vessels, and have an anti-oedematous effect. Aescin can also be used to reduce swelling in the case of bruises and fractures. The active principles from the Horse Chestnut are component parts of commercial pharmaceutical preparations dispensed in the form of pills, ointments, gels and injections. The extract from chestnuts can be used externally in the treatment of phlebitis. Use in folk medicine cannot be recommended nowadays apart from decoctions from the bark, leaves or buds, occasionally used for that purpose. The active principles found in saponins from chestnuts are poisonous for children and are therefore not recommended for paediatric use.

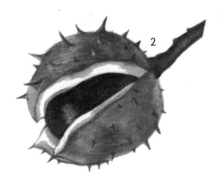

The Horse Chestnut (1) and its cultivated varieties are of far greater importance in garden landscaping as ornamental trees. They attain a height of up to twenty-five metres, have a dense, regular crown, large palmate leaves and, albeit briefly, lovely candle-shaped masses of flowers in May and June. The fruit is a large, globose, softly spiny capsule (2) containing from one to three shiny, brown seeds with a large pale 'navel' (3). The Horse Chestnut did not begin to spread to central Europe and westward until the late 16th century when the first specimens were grown in Vienna from seeds brought from

34

Istanbul by the botanist Charles de
l'Ecluse, better known under the
Latinized name *Clusius*. As far as
European medicine is concerned, the
Horse Chestnut was not used until the
late 19th century, initially by the
physician A. Arnault de Vevey, in
France, and later elsewhere.

WARNING: The seed of this tree is
poisonous and must be used only by
a registered medical practitioner.

3

1

Agrimony
Agrimonia eupatoria L.

Rosaceae

Members of the genus *Agrimonia,* numbering some fifteen species, are distributed chiefly in the temperate zone of the northern hemisphere. Common Agrimony, used for medicinal purposes, grows throughout Europe except for the extreme north, in Asia Minor, Iran, the Caucasus and north Africa. A similar, more warmth-loving species, *A. procera,* which is found only in Europe, is also collected for the drug. Both species contain amounts of similar active principles. Only the densely leaved flowering top parts are collected, leaving the woody, leafless lower part of the stems which contain far smaller amounts of active constituents. These include catechol tannins, glycosidic bitter principles, flavonoids, and traces of essential oil, in other words relatively common active principles. Nevertheless, in combination they have a reliable stimulating effect in digestive disorders caused by lower acidity of the gastric juices. The drug is also used to treat diarrhoea and to alleviate gall bladder pains. It is taken in the form of infusion (one teaspoon of the drug to one cup boiling water) sipped slowly three to five times daily. The tea may be taken for long periods without side effects. The infusion prepared in this manner, or a decoction prepared from one to two tablespoonfuls per one cup water, is recommended for external use as a mouthwash following dental surgery and as a gargle in thrush. The drug is also used in bath preparations in view of its proven anti-inflammatory and bactericidal effect, e.g. in the case of stubborn skin diseases.

Common Agrimony (1) grows on hedgebanks, in woodland clearings, and in dry meadows and pastureland, often on lime-rich soils. It reaches a height of from thirty to one hundred centimetres, depending on the locality. The stem is erect, usually unbranched, and covered

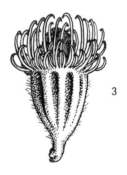

3

2

with both short and long hairs. The flowers with five golden-yellow petals (2) are arranged in a simple, scanty, spike-like raceme and are present from June until September. The fruit is an achene enclosed within a cup-shaped receptacle (hypanthium), which is

grooved and edged with a ring of
hooked bristles (3). The tradition of
Agrimony's healing properties dates
from ancient times. Nowadays it is
rapidly disappearing from the wild,
mainly due to the use of chemicals in
agriculture and forestry, and it is
therefore not surprising that commercial
cultivation for pharmaceutical purposes
is increasing. Agrimony is one of the
most important drugs available.

1

Couch-grass, Twitch
Agropyron repens (L.) P. BEAUV.

Gramineae

Couch-grass is a common perennial grass troublesome to farmers and the best known of the hundred species of the genus *Agropyron.* In Europe its distribution extends from Siberia, southward to north Africa. Only the long, slender, jointed, creeping rhizome, devoid of rootlets, is collected. When the fine rootlets as well as all soil remnants have been removed from the healthy, yellowish rhizomes they are dried and then arranged in neat bundles. This drug is often in short supply because its collection and preparation are difficult. Couch-grass's usefulness as a medicinal plant however does not make up for its harmfulness as a weed and that is why it is being consistently eradicated and is no longer so common in fields. The drug must be stored in air-tight containers because it readily absorbs moisture. It contains the polysaccharide triticin, mucilage, saponins, soluble silicic acid and principles with a bactericidal action. These constituents give the drug its specific diuretic properties and that is why it is used primarily in the treatment of prostate diseases, including benign tumours of the prostate gland. In addition to this the drug is used in various tea mixtures to stimulate the metabolism and harmonize its processes. The drug is used in the form of a decoction (one teaspoon of the crushed drug to one cup water, taken two to three times a day) or else simply finely crushed as is (one teaspoon of the drug added to a glass of tepid water, stirred, and drunk *always* before meals).

Couch-grass (1) has all the typical characteristics of the Gramineae family. It has a relatively shallow root system

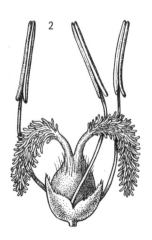

forming such a dense tangle of rhizomes that their weight taken from an area of one square metre equals 1.5 kg or more and their length over sixty metres. Growing from the rhizome is a stem up to one metre high with soft, flat, grass-like leaves, which is terminated by a narrow spike with fifteen to twenty deciduous spikelets. Each spikelet is composed of five flowers (2) that bloom from June until autumn. The grains have good powers of germination as soon as they ripen and remain viable for more than five years. Couch-grass is, therefore, self-propagating by means of the grains as well as rhizomes, which are highly resistant to frost. Some species of the genus *Agropyron* are used to combat erosion in sand dunes (e.g. *Agropyron junceum*) and sometimes also as forage grass.

1

Hollyhock
Alcea rosea L. cv. *Nigra*

Malvaceae

Hollyhock is a cultivated species native to Asia Minor, where it probably came into being as a hybrid of certain oriental taxons. Only the cultivated forms are known, ranging in colour from white through pink and red to dark violet, and it is the flowers of these dark forms that are collected for the pharmaceutical industry. Fully opened flowers along with the calyx are gathered by hand in the second year of the plant's growth. The designation for these flowers in pharmacies is *Flos alceae,* the more correct term; however the older designations *Flos malvae arborae* or *Flos althae roseae,* are still used. The constituents include anthocyanic pigments, 6 to 8 percent mucilage, tannins, and flavonoids, which are in the green part of the flower called the calyx. The drug has expectorant properties and promotes healing of the mucous membranes in diseases of the upper respiratory tract. If used by itself, one tablespoon of the crushed drug is steeped in tepid water for two to three hours or else only briefly, (this being quicker but less effective), and the infusion is then taken up to five times daily. Much more common, however, is the use of Hollyhock in herbal tea mixtures for chest colds (*Species pectorales*), where besides having a therapeutic effect, it enhances the colour of the tea. Both the plant and drug were introduced into Europe during the Turkish invasions in the 16th century. Nowadays it is cultivated for the pharmaceutical industry on small-size tracts because picking by hand is time consuming and cannot be mechanized.

Hollyhock (1) is a biennial or perennial herb that in the second and ensuing years bears a thick stem sometimes more than two metres high ending in a spike-like cluster of large showy flowers up to eight centimetres across. The disc-shaped fruit, a schizocarp, separates into one-seeded nutlets when ripe. Of the plants of the mallow family used for medicinal purposes Hollyhock ranks third in importance. The two most important are Marshmallow (*Althaea officinalis*) and Mallow (*Malva sylvestris*) (2). All have the same uses, because their active principles are practically identical. The leaves of all the aforesaid species are sometimes attacked by rust (*Puccinia malvacearum*). Such leaves are not collected and are not used in the drug.

1

Lady's Mantle
Alchemilla xanthochlora Rothm.   Rosaceae

The genus *Alchemilla* includes a great number of described species and lower taxons, difficult to differentiate even for an experienced botanist, let alone for a person gathering medicinal plants. Lady's Mantle is considered to be an aggregate of species native to the temperate regions of Europe, western Asia, north Africa and southeastern Canada. Elsewhere it is an introduced species. The flowering stems and the basal leaves only are used for medicinal purposes. Undamaged paper sacks, protected from light, are used to store the drug. If overdried, Lady's Mantle readily crumbles. Its constituents include catechol tannins, glycosidic bitter principles, and flavonoids. The drug is relatively popular in folk medicine, even though detailed research has not come up with any extraordinary findings. It is generally used to treat menstrual pains, problems during the menopause, and vaginal discharges and is also recommended for nonspecific digestive disorders accompanied by diarrhoea and spasms as well as for inflammation of the urinary tract. Internally, Lady's Mantle is generally administered in the form of an infusion (one teaspoon of the drug to one cup boiling water) taken three times daily, externally it is more commonly used in the form of a decoction (two tablespoons of the drug to one cup water) as a gargle in inflammation of the mucous membrane of the mouth and throat, in bath preparations and in compresses for boils and phlebitis. Treating conjunctivitis with Lady's Mantle runs the risk of infection and should therefore be done *only under the supervision of a physician.*

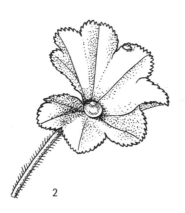

2

Lady's Mantle (1) is a perennial herb which grows to a height of thirty centimetres. It can be found, sometimes in abundance on damp banks, in subalpine meadows and in meadows bordering streams. The leaves are long-stalked, palmate to nine-lobed, circular in outline and serrated on the margin. Typical of this plant is the oozing of droplets of water onto the surface of the leaf (2), hence the medieval name for the plant, 'Heavenly Dew'. The nondescript greenish flowers (3 — closed, 4 — open) are without petals but have a calyx and epicalyx and are arranged in minute clusters (5). The fruit is an achene. The Latin name of the plant indicates its link with alchemy. Alchemists purportedly believed the drops of water exuded on the leaves had extraordinary medicinal as well as magical powers.

5

3

4

1

43

Marshmallow
Althaea officinalis L.

Malvaceae

Marshmallow grows on salty soils in Europe and western and central Asia, mainly in broader river basins from the middle reaches of the Danube to the Southern Urals, growing wild in many places. In the northeastern USA it grows in salt marshes by the seacoast. Marshmallow is a widely distributed, popular medicinal plant used in great quantities and therefore commercially cultivated. Its cultivation dates from as far back as medieval days when it was grown in monastery and country gardens. Marshmallow has long been used in the form of syrup to treat coughs and inflammation of the upper respiratory passages. It is used less widely in the form of an infusion for asthma, stomach and intestinal disorders and for colicky pains accompanied by diarrhoea in children. The roots and leaves are the parts used for pharmaceutical purposes. The main constituent is mucilage, others include starch, mineral salts and flavonoid compounds. The roots contain a greater amount of mucilage and for that reason are preferred for pharmaceutical purposes and are best collected in autumn when they contain the greatest amount. The drug from the roots as well as from the leaves should be steeped several hours (best of all overnight) in tepid, preferably cooler water, two teaspoons to one cup water, taken two to four times daily. The leaves are administered as herbal tea mixtures, for treating coughs, in compresses and poultices to soften oedemas, and as a soothing gargle in stomatitis.

4

This velvety felted perennial (1), which may reach a height of more than one metre, prefers damp conditions. It has a thick branched root and unbranched or slightly branched stems with flowers arranged in irregular racemes (a formation similar to that of hyacinth or lily of the valley) in the axils of the upper leaves. The flowers (2 — longitudinal section, 3 — view from below) are five-petalled. The stamens have purple anthers and the filaments are united in a central hollow tube through which the styles grow. The ovary with ten carpels develops into a disc-shaped fruit that splits when ripe. Rust (*Puccinia malvacearum*) (4) often attacks the leaves which are then not suitable for medicinal use. Because of its high concentration of mucilage and starch, Marshmallow root is also used in cosmetic emulsions and creams.

2

3

1

45

Dill

Anethum graveolens L. var. *hortorum* ALEF.   Umbelliferae

Dill is one of the two species of the genus *Anethum*. It grows in the wild from the eastern Mediterranean region to India and is used mainly as a vegetable and seasoning herb. It was popular with the Egyptians along with other ancient civilizations. Charlemagne included dill in a list of medicinal plants he thought ought to be cultivated, but in central Europe its cultivation dates only from the late Middle Ages. The fruits, which are collected when they turn brown and begin to ripen, and flowering stems are the parts used medicinally. They contain an essential oil which includes carvone and other components which give it a fragrance that distinguishes it from the essential oil of caraway, in which carvone is likewise the principal constituent. Dill promotes the flow of digestive juices, stimulates the appetite, relieves indigestion and stomach cramps and promotes undisturbed sleep. In folk medicine it is recommended for headaches and insomnia and also has a diuretic action. It is used in the form of an infusion (one teaspoon of the crushed fruits to one cup boiling water taken three times a day half an hour after meals or one cup of tea prepared in this manner taken before going to bed). The drug's use as an antiseptic in diseases of the upper respiratory passages is rejected nowadays because it is much less effective than other preparations. Dill is used mainly as a culinary herb, where its medicinal properties are naturally fully utilized. Seasoning food with dill makes it more appetizing and more digestible with the added bonus of a high vitamin content, if the top parts of the plant are used.

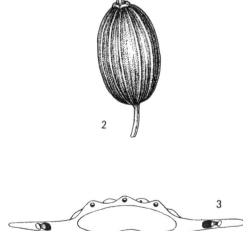

Dill (1) is a sparsely leaved, annual herb which grows to a height of more than one metre. The leaves are multipinnate and feathery and, like the hollow stem, smooth and as if covered with a bloom. The small yellow flowers are arranged in a similar fashion to a cowslip. The fruit is a flat, elliptical double achene with winged edge and five prominent ribs (2). Located between the ribs are minute channels containing essential oil, up to six percent in cultivated forms (3). Dill is an essential ingredient for pickling gherkins and other vegetables, and is also used as seasoning in salad dressing and with other foods. Because of this it is cultivated not only in home gardens but on a commercially large scale. Remnants of the harvest are sometimes used to distill the essential oil. Dill rarely becomes naturalized.

46

1

47

Garden Angelica
Angelica archangelica L. Umbelliferae

Garden Angelica is the most familiar of the fifty species that make up this genus. Native to the northern hemisphere in Europe and Asia, from the Arctic to the temperate zone, it grows more abundantly in the northerly regions in mountains and foothills, whereas farther south it is found only in mountain districts. The drug is obtained from the rhizome and roots and occasionally from the fruits or young stems. The large consumption of the drug from as far back as medieval times resulted in its current cultivation on a commercial scale with several varieties being developed for this purpose. The principal constituents are an essential oil with antiseptic properties, bitter principles, coumarins and furocoumarins. The drug from the root is widely used in treating stomach and bowel disorders, but its primary use is as an aromatic tonic with comprehensive action in treating lax function of the stomach and bowel caused by neuroses, dyspepsia, and lazy digestion accompanied by flatulence. For these complaints, one teaspoon of the crushed root per cup of water in the form of an infusion or briefly boiled decoction is taken twice daily before lunch and supper, slowly by spoonfuls. Besides its use in folk medicine in the form of an infusion and tincture Angelica is far more widely used by commercial distilleries to make bitter stomachic liqueurs such as Benedictine and Chartreuse, originally made in medieval French monasteries. Antirheumatic ointments containing Angelica are used only rarely nowadays as they were often found to cause skin rashes.

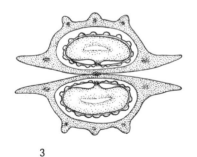

3

A biennial herb, Garden Angelica (1) is one of the giants of the parsley family. It grows in damp conditions, in meadows, gullies and by forest streams in mountain districts, less abundantly in foothills. During the flowering season from June till August it has a tall, thick, hollow stem more than two metres high. The basal leaves are large with long stalks, the stem leaves have inflated sheathing leaf-stalks. The large collective flower contains up to forty small, umbrella-shaped honey-scented flowers with greenish-yellow corolla and long protruding stamens. The fruit is an elliptical, pale yellow, double achene (2)

1

2

with two membranous wings on the
edge, clearly evident in the cross-section
of the fruit (3). In some parts of Europe
the young green stems, cut into rounds
and candied, are used to decorate cakes.

Greater Burdock
Arctium lappa L.

Compositae

Greater Burdock is native to the temperate regions of Asia. It is distributed throughout Europe but is probably not indigenous. In America it is an introduced species. Its roots which are collected in the wild and cultivated, are still used medicinally and the drug is still designated by its medieval name *Radix bardanae*. The fact that it is cultivated reflects the relatively large consumption of the drug. The constituents include unstable polyacetylenic compounds with antiseptic and fungicidal properties, also bitter principles, tannins, plus glycosidic lignan-type substances and traces of an essential oil and therefore the drug should be stabilized with alcoholic vapours or by boiling it briefly before drying. The aforesaid group of substances explains the relatively successful action of the drug. An infusion or briefly boiled decoction prepared from one teaspoon of the crushed drug per one cup water can be taken three times daily for gastritis, ulcers, liver and gall bladder disorders and early stages of diabetes. The drug is also used as a diuretic and to induce perspiration. A decoction made from one tablespoon of the crushed drug per half litre water can be used for bathing ulcers and eczemas of unidentified origin. The oil extract made from the drug or from the fresh root is used in preparations said to prevent baldness. Similar species with equally effective properties are also collected for the drug market, e.g. Lesser Burdock (*Arctium minus*) and Woolly Burdock (*Arctium tomentosum*), as well as hybrids of the two.

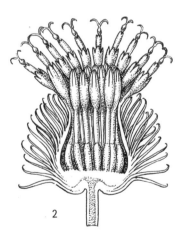

2

Greater Burdock (1) is a large biennial herb reading a height of one hundred and eighty centimetres with creeping, fleshy root. It is found in waste places, ditches by hedges and by waysides, mainly on deep, rich but neglected soils from lowland to submontane elevations. The basal stalked leaves are up to half a metre long. The leaf stalks, as well as the stems, are filled with pith. The flowering period is from July till September. The globe-shaped flowerheads contain numerous dark purple, tubular, five-petalled, disc florets. Clearly evident in the schematic longitudinal section (2) are the narrow encircling bracts, toothed at the base

50

1

3

and terminated by a hooked tip. These enable the dispersal of the flowerheads, which stick to the fur of animals, and are carried great distances. The fruit is a flattened, black achene with a pappus comprising several rows of hairs (3).

WARNING: This remedy used in excess may lead to a symptomatic crisis in severely toxic conditions or where digestive or bowel functions are deficient. Dosage should start cautiously and be increased as appropriate.

Bearberry
Arctostaphylos uva-ursi (L.) SPRENG.

Ericaceae

Bearberry is distributed in the temperate zone of the northern hemisphere, its range extending in the north to the Arctic and more rarely to the mountains of southern Europe and the Caucasus. The leaves are collected by stripping, solely in the wild. Field cultivation has so far been thwarted as this requires the planting of rooted cuttings which are costly to prepare. The drug is imported chiefly from Scandinavia, the USSR, and the Pyrenees. It contains arbutin (up to 14 percent), which produces the antiseptic component hydroquinone and D-glucose following ingestion. Other constituents include methylarbutin, a large concentration of tannins (up to 19 percent) and flavonoids. Due to the hydroquinone and ancillary substances the drug acts as an excellent disinfectant of the urinary passages but is not a diuretic. It cannot therefore be prescribed for acute inflammation of the bladder as it tends to have an irritant effect; it is used mainly in the treatment of chronic urinary diseases. When administering the drug, which should be finely crushed, it is necessary to observe two conditions. Tepid, never hot water should be used for steeping so that tannins, which cause nausea, vomiting and constipation, are not absorbed by the water. In order that the effective component hydroquinone be released from the arbutin, the urine must be alkaline. This may be achieved by taking a little soda bicarbonate (as much as will fit on the tip of a knife) along with the infusion. The dosage is one teaspoon of the drug to one cup water taken three to four times daily, in small drafts. *The drug should not be taken during pregnancy.*

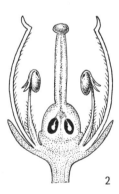

2

3

Bearberry (1) is a low shrub with long, creeping, densely leaved stems with ascending branchlets. In central Europe it is a relatively rare plant growing in small masses in open pine woods and heaths as well as in rock recesses, always in a location protected from frost. The leaves are leathery, glossy dark green on the upper surface and pale green on the underside. The arrangement of flowers is similar to that of a hyacinth with three to twelve flowers. They have an urn-shaped corolla coloured white to pink and stamens with purplish anthers (2 — longitudinal section). The fruit (3) is a globe-shaped, dark red stone fruit with five seeds inside. In favourable conditions a small number of plants may form a dense carpeting ground cover and may even include specimens that are a hundred years old. If the main root is destroyed however, the whole plant dies.

WARNING: This drug should be avoided where the kidneys are affected.

1

53

Arnica, Mountain Tobacco
Arnica montana L.
Compositae

The genus *Arnica* numbers some thirty species, all distributed in the northern hemisphere. *Arnica montana* is indigenous to Europe where it grows at higher elevations. It is a gravely endangered species and therefore protected in many countries. Because of its increasingly widespread use as a medicinal herb, efforts are being made to grow it or the more readily cultivated North American species *Arnica chamissonis*. Although the flowers are primarily used for medicinal purposes, the drug from the flowerheads, including the involucre, is more generally available. The rhizomes with their roots are no longer used for pharmaceutical purposes. Because of the drug's reputation in folk medicine the constituents have been thoroughly investigated and a great number have been isolated. The most effective, perhaps, is the group of pseudoguayanolids, flavonoids, isomeric alcohols and carotenoids, supplemented by an essential oil and tannins. Combined, these constituents have a stimulating effect on a heart muscle that is fatigued and receiving an insufficient supply of blood, and also on the circulatory system, comparable to that of Hawthorn, the difference being that the effect of Arnica is more rapid and poses a greater risk of overdosage. *For that reason it is dangerous to use the drug without consulting a physician and it must never be used to treat children or the elderly.* Externally it has an antiseptic, anti-inflammatory and healing effect. The use of the diluted tincture externally as a home remedy for bathing wounds to hasten healing is still widespread, as is its application to bruises. Only the drug's relative rarity prevents its being more widely used in therapy.

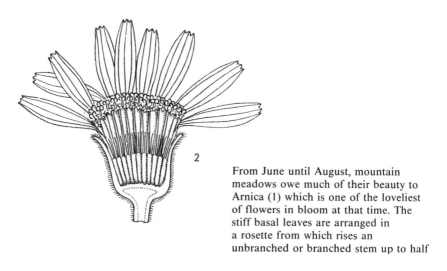

2

From June until August, mountain meadows owe much of their beauty to Arnica (1) which is one of the loveliest of flowers in bloom at that time. The stiff basal leaves are arranged in a rosette from which rises an unbranched or branched stem up to half

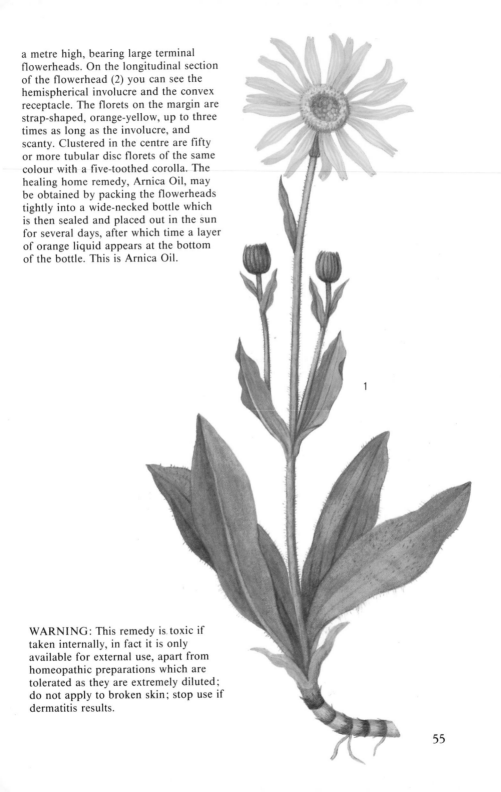

a metre high, bearing large terminal flowerheads. On the longitudinal section of the flowerhead (2) you can see the hemispherical involucre and the convex receptacle. The florets on the margin are strap-shaped, orange-yellow, up to three times as long as the involucre, and scanty. Clustered in the centre are fifty or more tubular disc florets of the same colour with a five-toothed corolla. The healing home remedy, Arnica Oil, may be obtained by packing the flowerheads tightly into a wide-necked bottle which is then sealed and placed out in the sun for several days, after which time a layer of orange liquid appears at the bottom of the bottle. This is Arnica Oil.

1

WARNING: This remedy is toxic if taken internally, in fact it is only available for external use, apart from homeopathic preparations which are tolerated as they are extremely diluted; do not apply to broken skin; stop use if dermatitis results.

Wormwood
Artemisia absinthium L.

With its more than three hundred species, the genus *Artemisia* is one of the largest in the northern hemisphere. These plants are often dominant in the steppes and semi-deserts of central Asia, north Africa and California. Wormwood is a European and west Asian species of the temperate zone, its range extending to the mountains of the subtropical regions. The flowering, densely leaved top parts only are used. They are collected in the wild or from cultivated plants where these are grown as an essential raw material for the food industry. The constituents include an essential oil with thujone and azulene as its principal components, and guayanolide bitter principles. These are the effective components of this aromatic, bitter drug, which are useful in cases of lax stomach and gall bladder function, insufficient secretion of gastric juices, and stomach prolapse plus all the accompanying symptoms such as lack of appetite, distaste for certain foods and ensuing neuroses. The drug is used in the form of an infusion (one teaspoon to one cup boiling water taken three times daily in small drafts half an hour after meals) or in the form of an alcohol extract (twenty to thirty drops in a glass of water taken three times daily). The drug also relieves flatulence, increases the flow of bile, eases stomach cramps, and alleviates lesser gall bladder problems. The favourable action of three to four week Wormwood therapy in treating the after effects of bouts of flu, infections and operations on the autonomic nervous system is well known.

2

Wormwood (1) is a bitter aromatic perennial herb of tufted habit with silvery-felted shoots reaching a height of up to one metre and sometimes becoming woody at the base. The stems are more sparsely leaved below and more densely leaved towards the tip. The leaves are grey-felted on either side with submerged glands containing essential oil. The inflorescence consists of numerous, short-stalked flowerheads (2). All the florets in the flowerhead are tubular and coloured bright yellow. The fruit is a small, grooved achene without a pappus. Other species of *Artemisia* are used for pharmaceutical purposes as well as in folk medicine, e.g. Southernwood (*A. abrotanum*) and Tarragon (*A. dracunculus*). They are likewise important culinary herbs.

WARNING: Wormwood must not be used without medical supervision as the thujone in the essential oil affects the central nervous system if taken for long periods. It should never be taken by people suffering from liver disease.

1

Silver Birch
Betula pendula ROTH
Betulaceae

The genus *Betula*, distributed throughout the northern hemisphere, includes some forty species, of which two, Silver Birch and Downy Birch (*B. pubescens*), are of pharmaceutical interest. The leaves of both are used medicinally. The drug contains mainly glycosidic substances such as the flavonoid hyperoside, and traces of bitter principles. The concentration of saponins is arguable but most authorities include them among the constituents. The essential oil contains bactericidal components and is concentrated primarily in the leaves and buds when they are young. These are used only very occasionally for pharmaceutical purposes, so that the commercial drug, made from mature leaves, contains only traces of essential oil. Birch leaves are diuretic, induce perspiration and are also effective in relieving rheumatic pains. Although the diuretic action is sometimes the subject of doubt it is taken into account in a great number of preparations. An infusion made from one tablespoon of the crushed drug per one cup water taken two to three times daily is the recommended dose. The drug's advantage is that it does not irritate the kidneys in chronic inflammation of the urinary passages. In folk medicine it is also considered excellent for relieving rheumatism and sciatica and is often found in herbal tea mixtures used for this purpose. Externally the infusion from the drug extract is recommended for hair treatment and the use of birch sap in the hair cosmetics industry, shampoos etc., is equally well known.

3 ♀

The genus *Betula* includes not only large trees but also shrubs and even dwarf birches that are a typical component of the arctic tundra. All are undemanding and very hardy, woody plants. The Silver Birch (1) is a familiar tree ranging from ten to thirty metres in height, with an erect trunk which has smooth silver-white bark at its top that peels off in papery strips and blackish, deeply fissured bark towards the base. The twigs are covered with waxy warts known as lenticels. The leaves are long-stalked, thin, and heart- or lozenge-shaped in outline, vivid green on top and a paler green underneath. The flowers, appearing from April to May, are unisexual and arranged in catkins. The male catkins (2) are sessile, cylindrical and scanty; each flower has a set of bracts and two stamens. The

2 ♂

1

female catkins (3) on the lower branches
are stalked and thick; the individual
flowers are uncovered. The fruit—
a smooth-skinned, two-winged achene
—develops inside a two chambered
ovary.

Borage
Borago officinalis L.

Borage is native only to the Mediterranean region from Spain to Turkey. Nowadays it also grows in the warmer regions of western, central and eastern Europe as well as Western Asia, where it often becomes naturalized. It was introduced in this way to other continents. It was spread by the Arabs in the Middle Ages, later becoming popular as a culinary herb and as food for bees. Only the flowering top parts are used medicinally. These are very fragile and watery and therefore difficult to dry as they can go mouldy. They contain mucilage, tannins, alantoin, aromatic substances with a cucumber-like scent and silicic acid. As a drug, Borage is not of vital importance medicinally, but its value should not be underestimated. Its chief properties are diuretic, antiseptic, and anti-inflammatory and it is suitable as ancillary therapy in the treatment of urinary infections in children and the elderly. It is used in the form of a cold-water infusion (one tablespoon of the crushed drug to one cup water taken two to three times daily in small drafts). Its purported favourable effects on the central nervous system have been noted, for instance, in menopause, but have never been adequately proven. As a home remedy Borage is recommended for nervous exhaustion and depression, as a fever remedy and externally as a solution for bathing minor inflammations of the mucous membranes and for healing skin injuries. For this purpose a solution of two tablespoons of the drug to half a litre of tepid water is recommended. Borage is also a popular culinary herb known for its delicate, distinctive flavour.

2

Borage (1) is an annual herb reaching a height of seventy centimetres, with juicy shoots and cucumber-like scent and taste. It requires rather damp, sandy to loamy, fairly nourishing and lime-rich soil in a sunny or partly shaded situation. It is covered with rough, stiff, bristly hairs on its stems and leaves. The flowers, which occur from June until August, grow in loose, terminal monochasial broad, cone-shaped clusters and have a bright blue wheel-shaped corolla with white outgrowths in the corolla mouth. The stamens have reddish-violet anthers. The fruits are keeled, ribbed, rough, pale brown nutlets (2). During the flowering period, Borage produces large quantities of nectar, as much as 2.5 mg per flower in one day, and for that reason is a very important food plant for bees.

1

61

Pot Marigold
Calendula officinalis L.

Compositae

The genus *Calendula* is native to the Mediterranean region from the Canary Islands to Iran. It numbers some twenty species of which Pot Marigold is the best known and most widespread. It is grown for ornament, as food for bees, and for its medicinal properties and was grown in early medieval days in monastery gardens north of the Alps. The first record of its cultivation as a medicinal herb, by Abbess Hildegarde von Bingen, dates from the 12th century. The flowerheads, either whole along with the green outer bracts but without the stalk, or else only the outer ray florets removed from the flowerheads after drying are used in medicines. Dark orange-red double cultivars are preferred. The drug contains natural pigments, carotenoids, saponins (calenduloside), polyenes, alcohols and traces of an essential oil. Together these constituents have an anti-inflammatory and antiseptic action, stimulate the flow of bile, and have a mild antispasmodic effect. The drug is used in the form of an infusion made from one teaspoon of the drug to one cup boiling water and taken up to six times daily, in the treatment of gall bladder and digestive complaints. It is used far more extensively for healing stubborn wounds which should be bathed with an infusion prepared from two tablespoons of the drug to half a litre of water. Bathing with the infusion promotes the granulation of damaged tissue and is successfully used also in the treatment of minor burns, frostbite, varicose ulcers etc. Extracts from the drug are used in healing ointments and cosmetic preparations with soothing anti-inflammatory properties.

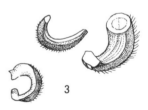

3

2

Pot Marigold (1) is a common annual or biennial herb with a balsam-like fragrance and reaches a height of between twenty and seventy centimetres. The leaves are sticky and rough to the touch. The stems are topped by single or double flowers varying in size from three to seven centimetres across and coloured pale yellow (2) to red-orange. The fruits are achenes of widely diverse shape—a textbook example of so-called

1

heterocarpy or bearing different fruits
(3). From the margin to the centre of the
flower there are roughly five different
forms of achenes ranging from the large
crescent-shaped achenes with hooked
teeth on the margin to the ring-like ones
in the centre. Used as a home remedy is
so-called 'Pot Marigold oil', analogous
to Arnica oil both in the way it is
prepared and in its application.

Shepherd's Purse
Capsella bursa-pastoris (L.) MEDIK.

Cruciferae

The genus *Capsella,* numbering five species, has a cosmopolitan distribution thanks to Shepherd's Purse, which is one of the world's most widespread weeds. Perhaps its use as a medicinal herb since as far back as ancient times was also due to its general availability and this tradition survives to this day in folk medicine. The flowering top parts, including the basal leaf rosette are collected for medicinal use at most times of the year. The constituents include biogenic amines (which give the drug its rather unpleasant odour), glycosidic substances such as diosmin, saponins, and common ancillary substances such as organic acids, sugars, etc. In folk medicine the drug has been used to check bleeding in gynaecological disorders, as a diuretic, and externally to treat eczema. Because it is generally taken as one of a number of ingredients in herbal tea, the effects of the drug are not always conclusive. The clotting effect is ascribed to diosmin, but this has not been clinically verified. Nevertheless favourable results have been obtained in the long-term treatment of uterine bleeding caused by uterine muscular disorders or bleeding caused by myomes during the preoperational period and is also recommended for the treatment of gravel in the urinary passages. It is prepared in the form of an infusion steeped for several hours in tepid water (one teaspoon of the crushed drug to one cup water) and taken two to four times daily. It is prepared in the same manner for bathing eczemas, but in this case two tablespoons of the drug are steeped in half a litre of water.

Shepherd's Purse (1) is an annual or biennial herb reaching up to sixty centimetres in height and exhibiting marked variation in form. It grows as a weed in fields, gardens, waste places and by waysides, mainly on nitrogen-rich soils, forming a basal rosette of leaves from which rises an erect, unbranched or branched stem bearing loose floral formations, similar to the hyacinth, throughout the year. The flowers grow closely together at first, later becoming more sparse. They are small, extremely inconspicuous, and coloured white to pink (2). The fruits, on the other hand,—triangular heart-shaped seedpods attached at one apex (3)—are striking and it is from these that the plant takes its name. The drug should not contain a large number of fruits, for this would serve as an indication of an undesirably late harvest. In China the young basal leaves are eaten as a salad.

2

1

3

65

Caraway
Carum carvi L. Umbelliferae

Caraway's origins are not known, but as a seasoning it enjoys worldwide popularity. Although native to many meadow plant communities in Eurasia, the caraway used for culinary and medicinal purposes is not obtained from plants found in the wild but only from those especially grown for this purpose. The cultivated types yield large quantities of a good quality drug obtained from the ripe fruit which is gathered from July until August. The main constituent is an essential oil (3 to 7 percent), which contains carvone, limonene—a bitter principle also found in orange and lemon seeds, and other substances which are responsible for Caraway's effectiveness in relieving flatulence, improving digestion following dietary lapses, alleviating spasms in diseases of the digestive system, and improving digestion. It is used in the form of an infusion (one teaspoon of the crushed drug to one cup boiling water taken three to four times daily in small drafts), more often as an ingredient of herbal tea mixtures which are used to treat flatulence. The distilled essential oil is an ingredient of the well-known *Aqua carminativa* and of caraway alcohol extract. This pharmaceutical form is only a small step away from Kümmel, a liqueur popular all over the world. Kümmel's use in treatment, however, depends on the patient's condition.

In the wild, Caraway (1) is an annual or perennial herb whilst cultivated forms are usually biennial. It has finely divided leaves and stems up to one metre in height, ending in umbrella-shaped flowers characteristic of the entire family. The flowers, which are present from May until July, are in five segments, with loose surrounding bracts and white or rose-tinted petals. The fruit is a rectangular double achene (2) that splits from the base into two crescent-shaped, brown achenes—the caraway seeds with which we are all familiar. In cross-section the achenes (3) have the shape of a pentagon with five low, rounded ribs. Located between the ribs are ducts containing the aromatic essential oil.

2

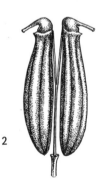

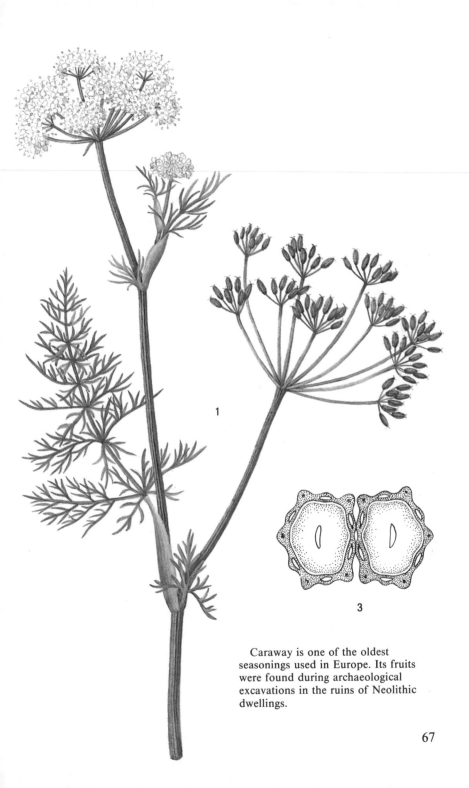

1

3

Caraway is one of the oldest
seasonings used in Europe. Its fruits
were found during archaeological
excavations in the ruins of Neolithic
dwellings.

67

Common or Lesser Centaury
Centaurium erythraea RAFN
Gentianaceae

The genus *Centaurium* comprises about forty species distributed in the northern hemisphere, South America and Australia. Common Centaury grows mainly in the temperate regions of Europe, in western and central Asia and in northwest Africa. In Europe it is an endangered species, not only due to the effects of industrialization but also because its flowering tops are widely collected for pharmaceutical purposes. Cultivating the plant would be a good solution but is difficult and costly. The drug is odourless and has a pronounced bitter taste. It has the same uses as Gentian and Buckbean, all three being among the most important drugs yielding bitter principles. The active constituents include the glycosidic bitter principles gentiopicroside, erytaurin, erythrocentaurin and traces of an essential oil. They have an excellent effect on increasing the flow of gastric secretions and thereby improving digestion, especially during convalescence and wherever the digestive system is sluggish, as well as stimulating the circulation. The drug is used in the form of an infusion (one teaspoon of the drug to one cup boiling water taken slowly by the spoonful three times daily about half an hour before meals). Should this method be poorly tolerated, it is possible to use *Tinctura amara* which contains an extract from the drug—twenty drops three times a day before meals. The drug also improves the appetite, especially in children. R. F. Weiss's prescription for children suffering lack of appetite is to drink an infusion made from 5 g of the drug in one glass of water before meals.

2

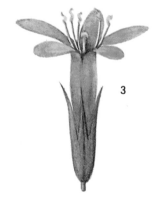

3

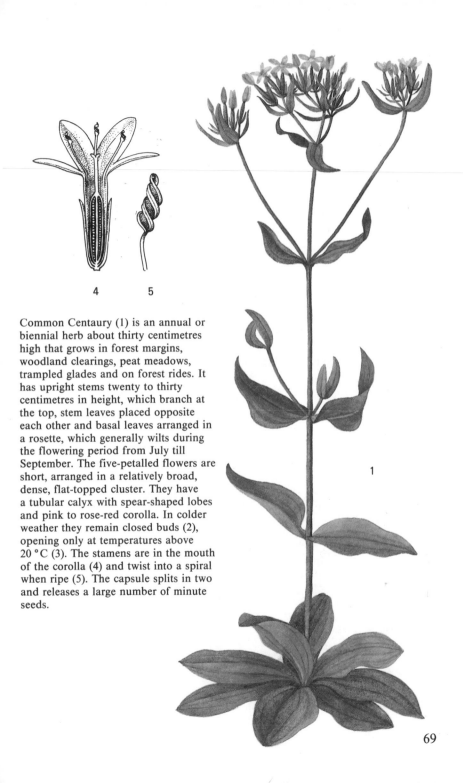

Common Centaury (1) is an annual or
biennial herb about thirty centimetres
high that grows in forest margins,
woodland clearings, peat meadows,
trampled glades and on forest rides. It
has upright stems twenty to thirty
centimetres in height, which branch at
the top, stem leaves placed opposite
each other and basal leaves arranged in
a rosette, which generally wilts during
the flowering period from July till
September. The five-petalled flowers are
short, arranged in a relatively broad,
dense, flat-topped cluster. They have
a tubular calyx with spear-shaped lobes
and pink to rose-red corolla. In colder
weather they remain closed buds (2),
opening only at temperatures above
20 °C (3). The stamens are in the mouth
of the corolla (4) and twist into a spiral
when ripe (5). The capsule splits in two
and releases a large number of minute
seeds.

4   5

1

Iceland Moss
Cetraria islandica (L.) ACHARIUS

Parmeliaceae

Iceland Moss grows in the arctic and temperate regions of the northern hemisphere; in the south generally only in mountains. It has been used in folk medicine for hundreds of years and in times of need also served as a food plant for northern peoples. Its use in modern medicine dates only from the 18th century when it was brought to the attention of medical circles by the two renowned botanists and physicians—K. Linné and G. A. Scopoli. The part of the plant which contains the active principles is the thallus (green shoot) and the drug is called *Lichen islandicus*. It contains up to 50 percent mucilage and bitter lichen acids. These substances are effective in treating disorders of the digestive system and inflammation of the upper respiratory passages. In digestive disorders the mucilage and bitter substances combine to stimulate the appetite and flow of gastric juices. This type of illness is treated with an infusion, which contains mostly bitter principles. It is prepared by pouring one cup of cold water over one teaspoon of the crushed drug and steeping it for several hours, best of all overnight. The infusion is then taken the following day—one cup three to five times daily. For diseases of the upper respiratory passages, in particular bronchitis, and other stubborn and exhausting coughs, it is recommended to steep the drug in the same manner and to take it two to three times a day, best of all together with an infusion from thyme. Lichen acids contained in the drug have similar bactericidal properties to those of antibiotics. It is also possible to take the drug, prepared in the form of pastilles, for coughs and hoarseness.

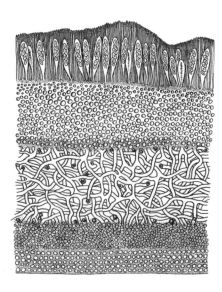

2

Iceland Moss (1) is a shrub-like lichen five to ten centimetres in height consisting of a stiff, branched thallus with incurved lobes. It grows by only a few millimetres per year and spreads mainly by means of broken-off thalli. In dry conditions the thallus is greenish-brown on the upper surface, in damp conditions olive-green; on the lower surface it is greyish-white. It is anchored to the ground at one spot, dies off at the base and grows at the top.

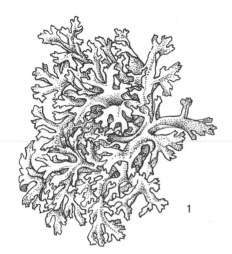

A schematic section of the thallus (2) shows how it is constructed. The upper outer layer is composed of dense fungus tissue, beneath this is looser tissue with clustered algae, then pith composed of loose, thick-walled fungus fibres. On the bottom there occurs once again an outer layer of fungus tissue, where bundles of fibres penetrate into the substrate. The fungus layer forms minute open-topped fruiting bodies that produce spores (3). If a germinating spore 'meets up' with a corresponding alga then it will give rise to the thallus of a new specimen.

1

3

Roman or Common Chamomile
Chamaemelum nobile (L.) ALL.

Compositae

Chamomile is a native plant in the wild only in southwestern and northwestern Europe (Spain, France, England and Ireland); in the eastern Mediterranean region, the Balkans and Crimea it occurs only secondarily. The quantities collected in the wild are not sufficient to fulfill the demand and so it is cultivated in many European countries, in Germany from as far back as the 16th century. Several frost-resistant double varieties have been developed and are grown from seedlings. The flowerheads without the stalk (*Flos chamomillae romanae*), are collected for pharmaceutical purposes. These contain an essential oil whose composition only partly resembles that of Scented Mayweed, also known as German Chamomile. It has a lower content of chamazulene and contains mainly esters of angelica acid. Other constituents of therapeutic value are flavonoids and bitter principles. They are anti-inflammatory, antispasmodic, and effective in the treatment of flatulence but these properties are less pronounced than those of Scented Mayweed. The drug is taken in the form of an infusion made from one teaspoon of the drug per one cup water taken three to four times daily. It cannot compete with Scented Mayweed for internal use, but has found wider application in external use. For this purpose it is used in the form of an infusion (one tablespoon of the drug to one litre of water) for bathing in the treatment of inflammatory diseases of the mucous membranes and skin with lesser risk of allergic reactions. It is also important in cosmetics as a hair tonic and component of herbal facial masks and as an ingredient of herbal mixtures used to make certain aperitifs and liqueurs.

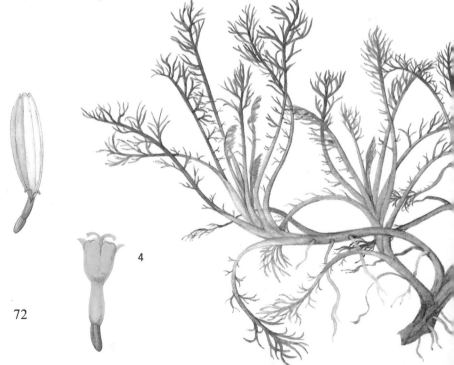

3

4

72

Roman Chamomile (1) is a very aromatic perennial herb ten to twenty centimetres in height. It forms spreading carpets with ascending flowering stems and shorter sterile shoots. It is more robust than Scented Mayweed (German Chamomile). The leaves are finely divided (two or three times pinnate), narrowly linear, and pointed. The plants flower from May till July, or even longer if the flowerheads are collected for the drug market, as they always produce new flowers afterwards. The flowers are arranged in long-stalked flowerheads at the tips of the stems (2). The involucre of the flowerhead is hemispherical with two or three whorls of bracts. The tongue-shaped ray florets are silvery-white (3), the disc florets are five-segmented and coloured yellow (4). Some cultivated varieties have only white tongue-shaped florets. The fruit is a smooth, shiny, triangular achene without a pappus.

WARNING: Roman chamomile is generally safe in the correct dosage but it must not be used by untrained persons as excessive dosage can cause vomiting and vertigo. It's sale is restricted to medical herbalists under the Medicines Act 1968.

2

1

Scented Mayweed, Wild or German Chamomile
Chamomilla recutita (L.) RAUSCHERT
Compositae

One of the most widely used medicinal herbs, Scented Mayweed is distributed throughout the whole world except for the tropical and arctic regions. It is thought to be native to southern and southeastern Europe. Flowerheads with stalks not exceeding two centimetres in length are gathered in succession during the summer before they are past their prime. Originally collected only in the wild, Scented Mayweed is nowadays cultivated on large tracts, several hectares in area, boasting excellent agrotechnology and mechanization. It contains two groups of active principles, the one consisting of essential oil (about 1 percent in cultivated varieties) with chamazulene, bisabolol and spiroethers, the second of flavonoids and other ancillary substances. It has an anti-inflammatory, vulnerary, and antispasmodic action and in digestive disorders has a beneficial effect on colicky pains accompanied by diarrhoea and painful flatulence. The drug is valuable in the treatment of digestive disorders in infants. It is equally valuable in child hygiene in the form of oils and skin creams. In view of its harmlessness the extent of its use is very broad, but does cause occasional allergic reactions. It is most widely used in the form of an infusion (one teaspoon of the crumbled drug to one cup boiling water, taken in small drafts several times a day). For baths, the recommended proportions are one to two tablespoons of the drug to one litre of water. There are hundreds of commercial preparations made from Scented Mayweed.

3

Scented Mayweed (German Chamomile) (1) is a common annual herb and often a troublesome weed by virtue of its biological and ecological character. Depending on the locality, it may be of small size, e.g. in the Hungarian plains, or may reach a height of more than half a metre in cultivated soils. The leaves are finely divided (two to three times pinnate). The flowers (longitudinal section—2) are arranged in flowerheads with a prominent convex to conical, hollow receptacle. The tongue-shaped ray florets are white, the disc florets yellow. The fruit is an achene without a pappus. A troublesome weed in fields

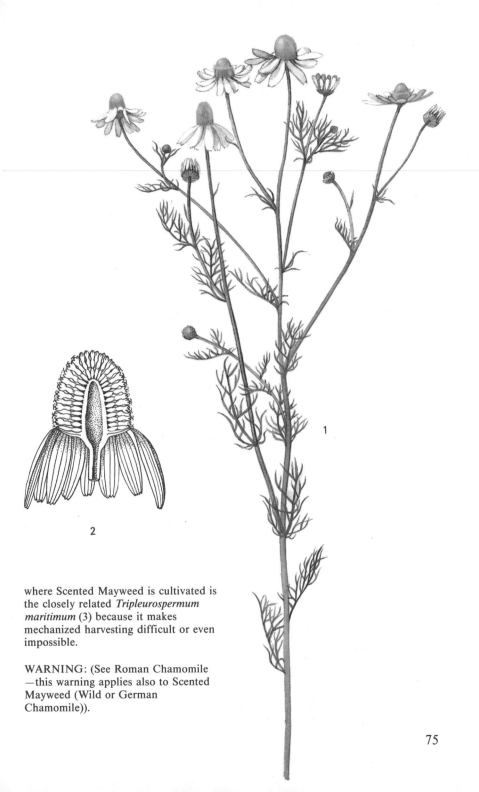

where Scented Mayweed is cultivated is
the closely related *Tripleurospermum
maritimum* (3) because it makes
mechanized harvesting difficult or even
impossible.

WARNING: (See Roman Chamomile
—this warning applies also to Scented
Mayweed (Wild or German
Chamomile)).

75

☠ Greater Celandine
Chelidonium majus L.   Papaveraceae

Greater Celandine is the only species belonging to this genus. It is distributed in the temperate regions of the northern hemisphere and was introduced to the Atlantic coast of North America. It is a weed of nourishing soils. The crude drug is made from the dried top parts, gathered when beginning to flower, but not the fruits. The plant's milky sap contains some twenty alkaloids, the principal one being chelidonine. Chelerythrine is the most toxic. The group of alkaloids and the presence of flavonoids have an antispasmodic effect on the digestive tract, stimulate the flow of bile, have a beneficial and soothing action in gall bladder, duodenal and stomach diseases, destroy infectious micro-organisms in the upper digestive passages, and have a sedative effect. The drug is generally used in the form of an infusion (one teaspoon of the crushed drug to one cup boiling water, taken two to three times daily). It is taken between the main meals, in other words in the morning and afternoon. The drug must not be more than a year old as the concentration of its active principles is not always reliable. A more certain method, therefore, is the use of a tincture from the fresh plant (thirty drops three times daily). Developments in pharmaceutics are sure to result in the production of preparations with a stable concentration of the group of alkaloids and flavonoids thereby eliminating the drug from therapy. Although the antispasmodic action of the drug also affects the bronchi it cannot replace effective antitussives. The alkaloids in the roots (mainly sanguinarine) are an effective component of mouthwashes used successfully in the treatment of periodontal (gum) diseases.

Greater Celandine (1) is a *poisonous,* perennial herb that reaches a height of up to one metre, depending on the location. It is very fragile and exudes an orange milky juice when bruised. The root is relatively small in comparison with the top parts and readily breaks off. The stem is hollow, the leaves alternate, pinnate, dark on the upper surface, and ash-grey-green on the underside. The flowers are bright yellow and arranged in umbels. The fruit (2) is a capsule which splits in two from the stalk upwards. The black dimpled seeds (3) have a fleshy white appendage that is a favourite food of ants, whereby they serve as reliable agents in the plant's distribution. The milky sap is still used externally to remove warts. The outcome is relatively successful if the sap is applied frequently to the warts — up to five times daily — and allowed to dry.

WARNING: Although specific doses of the drug have been noted here, this drug is *extremely poisonous* and should only be administered by a qualified physician.

3

Chicory, Wild Succory
Cichorium intybus L. var. *intybus*

Compositae

This genus includes three species of useful plants — Chicory, Endive (*C. endivia* L.) and *C. intybus* var. *foliosum,* all cultivated as salad plants. Chicory is native to the temperate and northern subtropical regions of Europe, western Asia and north Africa. It was introduced and became established in all parts of the world. The roots from both wild and cultivated plants are used medicinally. *C. intybus* var. *sativum* DC. is a variety of Chicory cultivated for use as a coffee substitute to this day. The drug is obtained by drying the roots at a moderate temperature. It contains glycosidic bitter principles and about 20 percent inulin (a white, starchy substance). These substances determine the drug's use as a stomachic, to stimulate the appetite and aid digestion. It is used in the form of an infusion (one teaspoon of the crushed drug to one cup boiling water) taken three times daily half an hour before meals. The drug is also recommended as an ingredient in herbal tea mixtures that 'purify the blood'. These are taken as a preventive therapy mainly in spring to correct the unsuitable composition of body fluids that might otherwise lead to illness and the accumulation of the causes of arteriosclerosis. Besides Chicory root, these tea mixtures contain the stems and leaves of nettle, birch leaves, and the flowers of elder. The abovementioned related vegetable plants, mainly because of their vitamin content and pleasant bitter substances, are, moreover, important ingredients in a proper diet.

Chicory (1) is a tall herb, exuding a milky sap when bruised. It grows by waysides, the edges of fields, embankments and in waste places and may reach a height of over one metre, depending on the location. It has a spindle-shaped tap root (2) and basal rosette of leaves, saw-toothed with lobes curving toward the base, from which rises a stiff, angled stem. The five-segmented flowers are clustered in heads. They appear from July until September and open only in the morning and in dry weather. They are coloured bright blue, including the stamens, very occasionally pink or

white. The fruit is an achene fringed
with a wreath of bristles, in reality
a modified calyx. The idea of roasting
Chicory roots originated in Europe after
1806 during the so-called Continental
Blockade proclaimed by Napoleon,
which made it necessary to find
a substitute for the hitherto imported
coffee.

WARNING: Excessive and continued
use of Chicory may impair function of
the retina.

1

Blessed Thistle
Cnicus benedictus L.

Compositae

Blessed Thistle is indigenous to the Mediterranean region of Europe, Asia Minor, Syria and Iran to Afghanistan. Elsewhere it has been introduced or grows wild, the seeds having been carried from cultivated areas. The flowering top parts are collected for the drug market before the flowers have passed their prime. The drug is obtained mainly from cultivated plants of several different varieties and *is very dangerous when handled in large quantities, mainly during drying and cutting when it may cause painful inflammation of the mucous membranes, eyes and skin. It is therefore necessary to wear at least glasses, gloves and a garment providing adequate cover for the body during manipulation with the drug.* Constituents include primarily the bitter principle cnicin, plus other common ancillary substances as well as flavolignans and traces of an essential oil. The drug purportedly also contains principles with an antimicrobial action. It is used to treat digestive disorders as an agent that promotes the flow of gastric juices and bile. The recommended treatment is by an infusion prepared from one less-than-full teaspoon of the crushed drug to one cup water, taken daily. It is also used in the form of an alcohol extract (tincture) — the dosage being twenty drops three times a day about half an hour before meals, washed down with a large glass of water. An occasional glass of Benedictine, which contains an extract of the drug, has been found effective during convalescence and also by elderly patients suffering from digestive upsets. Blessed Thistle should not be used in acute inflammation of the stomach or in the case of ulcers. It is one of the classic medicinal plants tested by centuries of use. New uses, e. g. in the treatment of herpes and rheumatism, have yet to be clinically tested.

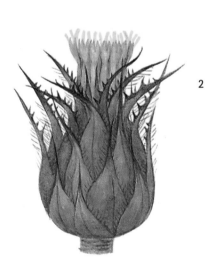

2

Blessed Thistle (1) is an annual herb with a richly branched, densely spiny stem, reaching a height of more than half a metre. It grows on sunny, stony banks, in waste places, and by waysides in warm districts in lowland regions, less often in hilly country. The leaves are saw-toothed, with lobes curving towards the base, toothed or cut about halfway towards the mid-rib into a number of pinnately arranged lobes, spiny on the margin, thickly hairy and sticky. The flowers (2), appearing from June until August, are arranged in terminal heads enveloped by the uppermost spiny stem leaves. They are tubular, five-segmented, and yellow. Those on the outside are sterile. The fruit (3) is a longitudinal, grooved, yellow-brown achene with toothed edge and double-ranked pappus.

3

1

81

Meadow Saffron, Autumn Crocus
Colchicum autumnale L. Liliaceae

The name of the genus *Colchicum,* which numbers sixty-five species, is derived from Colchis, an ancient country bordering on the Black Sea, now part of the Georgian Republic. Meadow Saffron, which is *extremely poisonous,* and grows throughout Europe from west to east, flowers in the autumn but the seeds do not ripen until spring. It is the seeds that are used medicinally. They contain some twenty highly toxic alkaloids, mainly colchicine. *The lethal dose for adults is a mere fifty mg and because of its great toxicity the drug is not used by itself at all.* Only preparations from pure alkaloids isolated from the seeds are used, the dosage only ever being prescribed by a physician. Colchicine is considered to be the only absolutely reliable agent for relieving the extremely painful inflammation of the joints in acute attacks of gout. Gout is a metabolic disorder characterized by an excessive proportion of uric acid in the blood, the salts of uric acid being deposited in the cartilage and ligaments of the body's joints. Therefore if the dosage is to be effective it ranges on the borderline of toxicity and any form of self-medication is out of the question. Besides the pure alkaloids also used is the alcohol extract from the seeds — *Tinctura colchici.* Colchicine, or the less poisonous demecolcine, are used as cellular poisons that inhibit cell division in the treatment of leukemia. Nowadays, however, preference is given to medicines containing alkaloids of the Madagascar species *Catharanthus roseus* (L.) G. Don. for such therapy. Colchicine remains important in plant genetics and selective breeding.

Meadow Saffron (1) flowers from September till October in damp — usually mown, fertilized or regularly flooded — meadows and marshes from lowland to submontane elevations. It is a perennial herb with a pear-shaped corm buried deep in the ground. The bud appearing on the side of the corm develops in summer into a short underground stem from which grow the flowers and ensuing spring leaves. The one to three violet-purple flowers (2) appear above the surface and bloom in autumn. The stamens inside the mouth of the flowers have orange anthers. At the time of flowering the ovary with numerous ovules is at the base of the perianth tube below the surface of the soil. After fertilization the underground stem begins to grow and its base thickens to form a new corm (3), from which broad spear-shaped leaves up to thirty centimetres in length emerge in spring. Between the leaves is an inflated capsule with numerous, very hard, globe-shaped seeds: cross-section of the capsule (4).

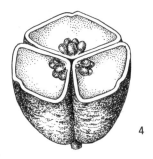

4

82

WARNING: Meadow Saffron is highly toxic and must never be self-administered. It is available only to registered medical practitioners.

2

3

1

83

Lily of the valley
Convallaria majalis L.

Liliaceae

Lily of the valley is the only species of this genus which grows throughout the northern hemisphere in the woods of Europe, Siberia, North America and Japan. It is a lovely, *though extremely poisonous* plant which is why its history as a medicinal herb is not lengthy. It has been used medicinally since 1856, when a group of glycosides, called convalamarin at that time, was isolated from the plant. The leaves and flowering stems are collected, being cut off with a knife at ground level. Yellowed leaves are ineffective. They contain up to 0.6 percent very effective poisonous glycosides, mainly convallatoxin, convallatoxol, and others. The plant's active principles regulate heart action and are hence used mainly in cardiology. It has been proved that there is a marked similarity between the action mechanism of glycosides from Lily of the valley and Foxglove. Glycosides from the former are, however, more effective. Lily of the valley has proved a worthy medicine because of the rapid onset of its effect and also because its cardiac glycosides do not accumulate in the body even during long-term use but are rapidly expelled in the urine. It is used in the treatment of circulatory disorders, cardiac insufficiency, especially in the elderly, and slowed heart rate. It is used only in the form of proprietary medicines containing the pure isolated glycosides or standardized extracts or very occasionally in the form of an infusion which should be prescribed only by a physician. Lily of the valley is a popular ornamental plant whose pleasantly aromatic essential oil is an important ingredient in the perfumery industry.

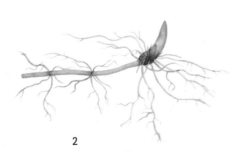

2

Lily of the valley (1) is a perennial herb of broad-leaved woods, woodland clearings, mountain meadows and thickets from lowland to mountain elevations. It has a creeping, branched, underground rhizome (2) that annually bears two elliptic leaves up to thirty centimetres in length alongside which rises an upright leafless stalk terminated by a loose one-sided spray of drooping flowers (3). The flowering period is in May and June. The flowers are bell-shaped, milky white or pink-tinged, with a pleasant fragrance. The longitudinal section (4) shows the arrangement of the flower with the stamens' thick filaments joined in their

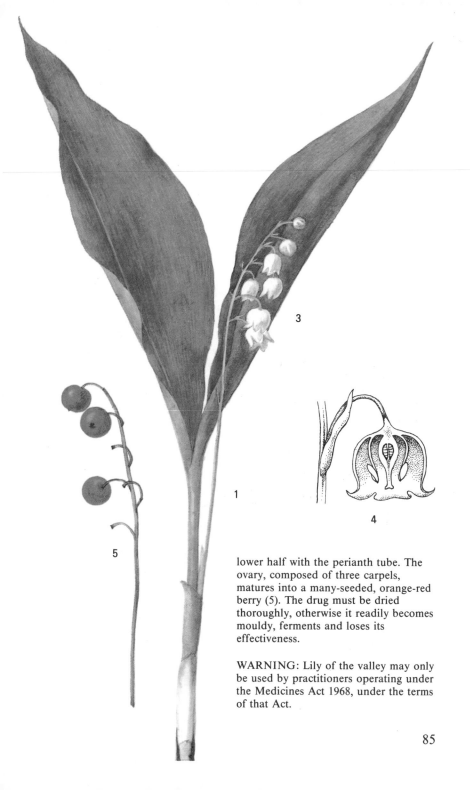

3

1

4

5

lower half with the perianth tube. The ovary, composed of three carpels, matures into a many-seeded, orange-red berry (5). The drug must be dried thoroughly, otherwise it readily becomes mouldy, ferments and loses its effectiveness.

WARNING: Lily of the valley may only be used by practitioners operating under the Medicines Act 1968, under the terms of that Act.

85

Coriander
Coriandrum sativum L.   Umbelliferae

Coriander is most probably indigenous to the Mediterranean region of Africa and Asia. Nowadays it is cultivated mainly as a culinary herb in all parts of the world, and often also grows wild. As with all other seasonings its popularity waxes and wanes as does the amount under cultivation. It is not of vital importance as a drug but it is widely used in Latin America. The ripe fruits are collected for medicinal purposes. They contain about 1 percent of a pleasantly aromatic essential oil with D-linalool as its main component. Like the other closely related species dill, caraway, anise and fennel, it is used in the treatment of digestive disorders generally accompanied by irritability, loss of appetite, and painful flatulence. Coriander may thus rightfully be designated scientifically as a stomachic, carminative, and mild spasmolytic. It is used in the form of an infusion (half a teaspoon of the crushed drug to one cup water) taken three times daily half an hour before meals. It is an ingredient of several types of the well-known distilled alcoholic liquor 'Carmelite drops', made by the Carmelite friars since 1610, whose principal constituent is distilled alcoholic liquor from balm. Externally it is used in the form of an alcohol extract rub for painful rheumatic joints and muscles. Coriander has a well-established place in the food industry as a seasoning that not only markedly improves the flavour and aroma of food but also makes heavier meats and pickled vegetables more digestible. It has the same effect when used in making breads and as an ingredient of curry-powder. It is also an ingredient of certain digestive liqueurs and is used to give aroma to certain beers. Coriander has been used by the people of India and the Mediterranean region for thousands of years.

Coriander (1) is an annual herb reaching up to eighty centimetres in height. In central Europe it occurs only as a cultivated plant or growing wild as a temporary escape. Unlike the pleasantly aromatic ripe fruits the top parts and unripe fruits have an unpleasant odour reminiscent of bed-bugs, caused by the organic compound trans-tridecene. The leaves are divided almost to the midrib, the upper ones finely so, with even linear segments. The white to reddish flowers are arranged in compound umbels of three to five umbellets. The fruit is a globe-shaped double achene (2) with low ribs, its two parts remaining joined even when ripe. The cross-section (3) shows two large ducts which produce essential oil on the broad flat base of each achene and small essential oil cells between the low ribs.

2

1

3

Midland Hawthorn
Crataegus laevigata (POIR.) DC.   Rosaceae

Midland Hawthorn is native to Europe and western Asia with a smaller area
of distribution in northwest Africa. The flowers are used by themselves, but
more often the flowers together with the young leaves, and very occasionally
the fruits. The drug from the flowers and leaves combined has a bitter taste;
the haws are mealy, sour and bitter. The constituents were thoroughly investigated recently and it was proved that they consist mainly of flavonoids and
so-called procyanidines, which are responsible for the drug's pronounced action. Also not to be overlooked are the basic triterpenic acids. Detailed research as to its effectiveness ranks this drug as one of the top phytotherapeu-
tic substances. It has a vasodilatory action on the coronary arteries thus
improving blood circulation to and strengthening of the heart as well as oxy-
genation of the blood. Its effect is not immediate but gradual and it therefore
is not a substitute for either nitroglycerine or digitalis glycosides. Secondarily, by strengthening the heart muscle, it lowers high blood pressure. This is
by no means a true hypotensive effect, but rather a mediated effect. The drug
has a beneficial action improving the heart rhythm in elderly patients that
have a weak heart and irregular heart rhythm. The drug's advantages are that
it can be administered safely for long periods and also that it is well tolerated. It is used in the form of an infusion (one teaspoon of the crushed crude
drug from the leaves and flowers to one cup water) taken in the morning and
evening. Herbal tea mixtures made from Hawthorn, Balm, Valerian and
Mistletoe can be recommended for their combined, soothing and hypotensive
effect. Extracts from Hawthorn are components of numerous commercial
preparations such as drops, pills, and injections.

2

Midland Hawthorn (1) is a thorny shrub
or tree reaching a height of up to ten
metres. It generally grows in scrub and
forest margins at lower, warmer
elevations. Occasionally it is planted out
intentionally and then often spreads by
itself. The leaves are alternate, stalked,
pinnatipartite, and coloured grey-green
on the underside. The flowering period

1

is from May till June. The floral arrangement consists of five to ten white five-petalled flowers and numerous stamens topped with red anthers. The fruit (2) is red, globe-shaped and apple-like with the remnants of the persistent calyx. Ornamental cultivated varieties with double white or red flowers are not suitable for pharmaceutical purposes.

Globe Artichoke
Cynara scolymus L.

Compositae

The Globe Artichoke occurs only in cultivation nowadays. In all probability it was developed by lengthy selective breeding from the Cardoon (*Cynara cardunculus*), which still grows wild in the Mediterranean region and has also been cultivated as a vegetable since ancient times. The leaves, which are odourless and have a bitter taste (*Folium cynarae*), are gathered during the flowering period. The constituents include the pleasant tasting glycosidic bitter principles cynarine and cynaropicrine, flavonoids with an anti-inflammatory action and tannins. In combination they have a beneficial effect on a diseased and weakened gall bladder and stimulate the secretion of bile by the liver as well as its detoxifying action. They lower the level of cholesterol in the blood and prevent excessive fatty deposits in liver tissue and the blood, thereby warding off arteriosclerosis. The drug prevents the formation of gall stones and lowers the level of sugar in the blood in incipient diabetes and diabetes in the elderly. It is recommended for eliminating undesirable after effects of treatment with antibiotics or sulfonamides. The aforesaid properties are more than enough to give this old/new drug a high rating. Nowadays many pharmaceutical specialties are made from Globe Artichoke but this in no way prevents its being used as a home remedy in the form of tea prepared by briefly boiling one teaspoon of the drug in one cup water and drunk two to four times a day before meals.

2

Globe Artichoke (1) is a large, perennial herb with upright, unbranched, felted stem, growing to a height of two metres. The large leaves, unlike those of Cardoon, are without spines and are grey-felted on the underside; the lower stem leaves are stalked, the upper ones stalkless. The relatively small, violet flowers are arranged in large flowerheads with a fleshy receptacle. The flowerheads may be even more than ten centimetres in diameter and are enclosed by overlapping, fleshy bracts. The fruit is an achene (2). Artichokes were known as a vegetable to the ancient Egyptians, Greeks and Romans, and in Rome they were an important item of the menu at feasts. Nothing is known about their cultivation in the

Middle Ages. It was not until the 15th
century that they made their appearance
in Italy and a century later in France.
They eventually made their way also to
central Europe, but there they are
readily destroyed by frost.

1

Thornapple, Jimsonweed, Stramonium
Datura stramonium L.

Solanaceae

When Thornapple was brought to Europe from America as an ornamental plant by the Spanish physician Francisco Hernandez in the 16th century, no one could have guessed that four hundred years later it would be considered a naturalized if not native plant in Europe. Nowadays it is distributed throughout Europe and in many countries it is also grown commercially. The leaves devoid of the stalks and very occasionally the seeds are used in drug production. *All parts of the plant are extremely poisonous*, containing more than 0.5 percent alkaloids, principally atropine, which derives from L-hyosciamine during the drying process, and scopolamine and must never be used unless prescribed by a physician. Other constituents include glycosidic ancillary substances, more or less the same ones as in Deadly Nightshade and Henbane. The alkaloids affect the central nervous system, mainly the brain. They relieve spasms of the smooth muscles in gall bladder and kidney colics and in asthmatic attacks. It is evident from this that the drug's main use is in the treatment of asthma and spasmodic coughs and also to suppress or at least mitigate tremors in Parkinson's disease and in the elderly. Even though it treats only the symptoms, it is a great boon to afflicted persons. In medicine today mostly only the pure alkaloids are used in special pharmaceutical preparations. The drug as such is used only rarely by asthmatics who inhale smoke from anti-asthmatic cigarettes or from specially prepared powders in which the leaves of Thornapple are an effective ingredient.

Thornapple (1) is an annual herb, often also an undesirable weed, that has become established in all parts of the world. Plants growing on nitrogen-rich soils, where it generally occurs, are robust, bushy specimens often more than one metre high with large, lobed, sinuate leaves. The large, white or violet-tinged, trumpet-shaped flowers with inflated calyx grow singly in the axils of the branches. The fruit is an upright, prickly, ovoid capsule with numerous black, kidney-shaped seeds. Also grown is the cultivar with spineless capsules (2), var. *innermis*, because this eliminates the danger of injury when gathering the leaves. Other species, differing markedly in the shape of the capsule among other things, are also of pharmaceutical importance commercially because of their greater concentration of alkaloids, chiefly scopolamine, e. g. *Datura metel* and *Datura innoxia* (3).

WARNING: Due to this plant's toxicity it may only be sold to practitioners under the terms of the Medicines Act 1968. If taken in excess it leads to cerebral depression and eventually, coma. It must not be administered during pregnancy, in cases of glaucoma, tachycardia, prostatic disease or with depressant drugs.

1

2

3

Round-leaved Sundew, Common Sundew
Drosera rotundifolia L.

The genus *Drosera* numbers some ninety species and its centre of origin is located in the southern hemisphere. Round-leaved Sundew is one of three species native to Eurasia that grow in poor acidic soils, mainly moorland. In view of its slight dimensions all parts of the plant, including the roots, are collected for the drug market — during the flowering period. As a matter of fact Sundew cannot be collected at any other time. It is a greatly endangered species due primarily to the disappearance of its natural habitats and to some degree also to ill-considered collecting. Round-leaved Sundew was used for medicinal purposes even in ancient times, when it was added to herbal liqueurs. The drug contains napthoquinone derivatives, mainly plumbagin, and ancillary substances. It is used for its specific antispasmodic effect in spasmodic, convulsive coughs and its beneficial effect in incipient arteriosclerosis and circulatory problems. In the case of arteriosclerosis it is necessary to consider long-term treatment. Because of the drug's limited availability it is no longer used in the form of an infusion so often. The dosage is one teaspoon of the drug to one cup boiling water taken three times daily in small drafts. In treating spasmodic coughs the drug has proved very effective in combination with Thyme in the form of an infusion made from five parts Thyme (flowering tops) and one part Sundew — a cup of the brew three to five times daily. Because of the limited supply of the drug from Round-leaved Sundew other species of *Drosera* are imported for the purposes of the pharmaceutical industry. Cultivation of the plant is also being considered.

2

Round-leaved Sundew (1) is a perennial, carnivorous herb with delicate filamentous roots that grows in moorland, the edges of moors and on dripping rocks. The leaves are arranged in a ground rosette and coiled in a spiral when young. They are long-stalked, almost circular, and covered with red, glandular hairs that secrete droplets of a sticky fluid containing digestive enzymes at their tips. These enzymes help digest the soft parts of insects caught and held fast by the sticky drops on the leaves. Rising from the leaf rosette is a slender leafless

stalk terminated by a loose monochasial
cluster of small white flowers, produced
from June till August. The fruit is
a capsule with numerous small seeds.
A like drug is obtained from other,
generally larger species with longer and
larger leaves such as *Drosera anglica,
Drosera capensis* and *Drosera paleacea*
(2).

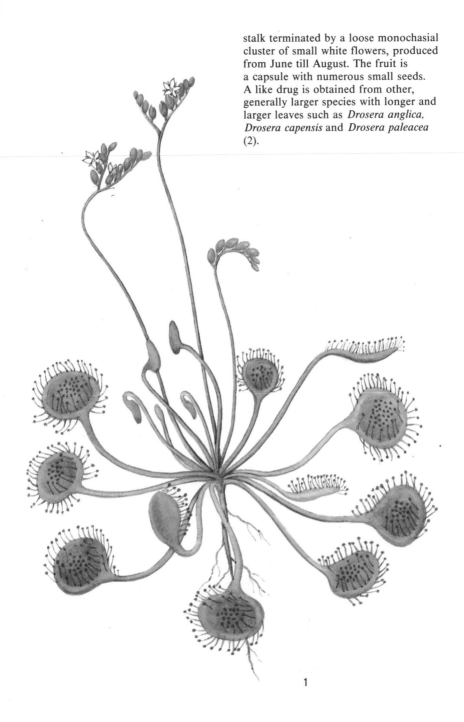

1

Male Fern
Dryopteris filix-mas (L.) SCHOTT

Aspidiaceae

This is a **poisonous** species of fern of variable shape that is widely distributed throughout the northern hemisphere. Used medicinally are the rhizomes together with the inseparable remnants of the frond bases. They contain numerous phloroglucin derivatives, which are very unstable. For this reason the drug obtained by drying loses its effectiveness quite rapidly. The drug is used mainly as an anthelmintic, in other words to eradicate intestinal worms, especially tapeworms and the diseases they cause. The best therapeutic effects have always been achieved by using not the dried but the fresh drug, or rather the extract from the drug. It was introduced into medical practice in the 18th century by the Swiss physician Peschier. Nowadays use of the drug is being abandoned primarily because of the availability of synthetic anthelmintics that are safer and better tolerated. However when these fail to produce the desired results the extract from the crude drug remains a more effective though more risky agent. The risk involved is damage to the liver and that is why the drug should never be administered in cases where the liver has been damaged or weakened, e. g. after hepatitis, and in children. Lowering the dosage for safety's sake is ineffective. Occasionally the decoction is used in the form of baths to treat fungus diseases. This drug is **toxic** and must never be taken unless prescribed **by a physician.**

Male Fern is a robust, shade-loving perennial fern of damp woods from lowland to mountain elevations. It has a scaly rhizome covered with rust-coloured hairs (1) and bearing a funnel-like arrangement of large fronds (2) on rather short, thick, reddish-brown stalks with chaff-like bracts. Rectangular and narrowing at each end, they are composed of as many as thirty alternately paired leaflets pinnately divided nearly to the midrib. From June till September there are two rows of sori (round groups of spore-cases) (3) on the underside of each leaflet enveloped by a kidney-shaped membranous shield and coloured greenish-white at first, later brown. The plant exhibits marked variability.

WARNING: This drug may only be used under medical supervision. Large doses may cause blindness or death.

96

1

2

97

Common Horsetail
Equisetum arvense L.

Equisetaceae

Horsetail grows mainly in the northern hemisphere, its range extending from the arctic region to Sicily, northern Iran, the Himalayas and China; also south of the equator where it was introduced. It spread most widely during the period when it was used for scouring pewter vessels. A field weed that spreads readily be vegetative means, it continually encroached on new territories. The sterile summer stems are used medicinally. They are odourless, lack any taste, and readily become mouldy if they are not thoroughly dried. They contain partially soluble silicic acid, saponins with a diuretic action, and flavonoids. The presence of alkaloids is not substantiated by objective proof. Its new repute in medical practice was promoted in the 19th century by the renowned phytotherapist and founder of hydrotherapy, Sebastian Kneipp. The drug's main use is determined by its diuretic action. It is administered in the form of an infusion (one teaspoon of the crushed drug to one cup boiling water taken three times daily) either by itself or in combination with other effective drugs (parsley, restharrow, and juniper). Other therapeutic treatment with the drug is determined by the beneficial effect of the constituents on the elasticity and firmness of ligaments and it is hence used after orthopaedic operations and also to treat painful conditions of the lower back muscles. Recommended forms of treatment are bathing with a preparation from the drug and taking it internally in the form of an infusion (two tablespoons of the drug to one litre water, steeped briefly or for several hours) taken four to five cups daily. The drug is no longer used for its purported beneficial effect in the treatment of tuberculosis because there are now proven effective medicines to treat the disease. The drug is also effective in treating rheumatism.

Common Horsetail (1) is a perennial vascular plant spreading by means of spores from the spring stems and asexually by means of the jointed rhizome. The fertile spring stems without chlorophyll as well as the green summer stems are annual. After the spores have been released, the spring stems dry up and the rhizome bears brittle summer stems from ten to fifty centimetres in height, grooved and branching in whorls. It is these that are collected for the drug market. Horsetail is found commonly on embankments, alluvium, and in ditches from lowland to mountain elevations and is a troublesome weed of damp meadows, fields and gardens. The stems of other quite similar species, e. g. *Equisetum sylvaticum* (2) and Marsh Horsetail (*E. palustre*), are **not** collected for the drug market since they are considered **poisonous** because they contain alkaloid bases.

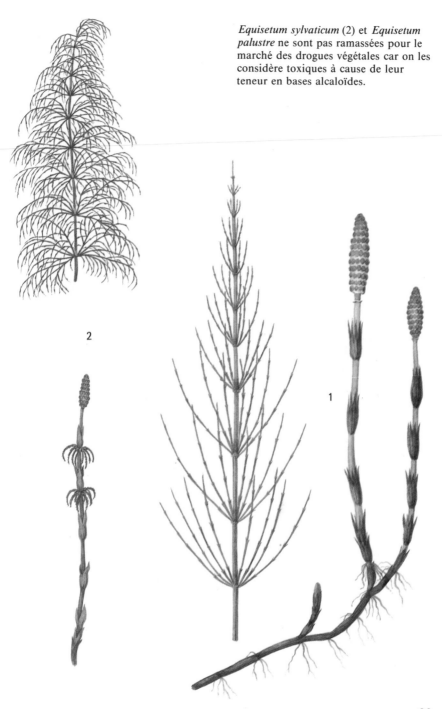

Equisetum sylvaticum (2) et *Equisetum palustre* ne sont pas ramassées pour le marché des drogues végétales car on les considère toxiques à cause de leur teneur en bases alcaloïdes.

2

1

Eyebright
Euphrasia rostkoviana HAYNE
Scrophulariaceae

This genus, found in the northern hemisphere, mainly in Europe, Siberia, and the Himalayas includes some two hundred species with only slight differences in form. All species of the *Euphrasia* type section are suitable for pharmaceutical purposes. The plant's generic name is derived from the Greek word *euphraino*, meaning to gladden, and it was used in ancient times to treat eye troubles. The parts used medicinally are the flowering stems. They contain flavonoids and the glycoside aucubin with marked healing, or granulation properties. The other constituents, primarily tannins and perhaps also an essential oil, promote the action of aucubin. The drug is used in the form of an infusion as an eyebath and in compresses applied to the eyes to treat inflammation of the eyelids, inflammation of the conjunctiva, and styes. It is also good for treating general tiredness of the eyes and all accompanying effects. The infusion is prepared from one tablespoon of the crushed drug to half a litre of boiled water. Compresses should be lukewarm, in the case of styes it is recommended to apply hot compresses. Place a pad, soaked in the infusion, on each eye and leave it there for at least ten minutes. For eyebaths, Eyebright is also used in combination with chamomile and fennel. The drug may also be taken internally to treat digestive disorders and inflammation of the upper respiratory passages (one teaspoon of the drug to one cup water, three times daily), and is also used as a raw material for commercial eye preparations.

Eyebright (1) is an annual, semiparasitic herb, usually of small size. By means of the haustoria on its roots, it attaches itself to the root systems of grasses and sedges and absorbs dissolved mineral substances from their conductive tissues.

The stems are ascending, with both glands and hairs at the nodes. The leaves grow in pairs opposite each other, each pair at right angles to that above and below and toothed on the margin. The flowers (2) are hermaphroditic, symmetrical, with four-toothed, bell-shaped calyx and two-lipped corolla coloured white to pale violet; sometimes there are purple stripes ('honey guides') on the lower lip and yellow spots at the entrance to the throat. The fruit, a capsule, splits in two to release the numerous small seeds inside. Some species produce two types of plant during a single growing season; this is known as seasonal dimorphism. The summer plants are small with unbranched stems and flower from May until June, the autumn plants are larger with greatly branched stems and flower from September until October.

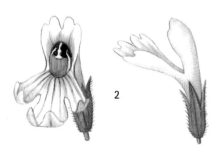

2

1

Common Buckwheat
Fagopyrum esculentum MOENCH   Polygonaceae

The genus *Fagopyrum* has two species, both native to central Asia, which occur in several self-adapted forms and cultivated varieties. Buckwheat was cultivated as a source of flour and as fodder for animals in the steppes of eastern Asia. In the 10th century it was already known in China and made its way to Europe in the Middle Ages with the invasions of the Mongols and Tartars. It was widely cultivated in Europe at first but gradually became less important. Of the present total of two million hectares under cultivation 65 percent occurs in the northern regions of the USSR, followed by China, Japan, India, the USA and South America. The top parts of the plant serve almost exclusively as raw material for the isolation of the flavonoid glycoside rutin (1 to 5 percent) which is used for treating circulatory disorders, haemorrhoids, varicose veins, varicose ulcers, etc. Rutin is an effective ingredient of many proprietary medicines for treating the aforesaid problems. Commercial preparations are preferred to the use of the crude drug, made from the dried top parts, exclusively, because in addition to rutin the stems also contain the toxic dianthrone fagopyrin, which causes inflammation of the skin, diarrhoea and spasms mainly in animals exposed to the sun. The disease is called fagopyrism and occurs in pigs and sheep that were fed buckwheat. The relatively large concentration of oxalic acid likewise makes direct use of the crude drug highly undesirable.

2

Common Buckwheat (1) is an annual herb with a hollow, angled stem that turns red as the plant matures. It reaches an average height of eighty centimetres. The leaves are stalked and broadly heart-shaped. The pinkish flowers are small and arranged in sprays at the joints between leaf and stem and in a terminal flat-topped spray in which the lower flower stalks are longer than those at the top. The fruit is a three-sided, brown achene (2) resembling a beech nut, and it is from this that the plant derives its German name. Besides Common Buckwheat, also grown in Europe as an admixture is Green or Tartary Buckwheat (*Fagopyrum tataricum*), cultivated for thousands of years in central Asia, for example in

Nepal. It gives lesser yields but is frost
resistant and generally has a greater
concentration of rutin. Its stem as well
as fruits remain green when ripe.

Fennel

Foeniculum vulgare MILL.

Umbelliferae

This, an extremely variable species, is indigenous in the area extending from the Mediterranean-Oriental region to India. Only the fruits from cultivated plants are used medicinally. They contain an essential oil with anethole and fenchone as the main constituents, flavonoids, coumarins, and ancillary substances. The drug is used to treat conditions that can be divided into two groups: firstly diseases of the upper respiratory passages where Fennel acts as an expectorant promoting the discharge of mucus from the bronchial tubes and exerting an anti-inflammatory action; secondly in treating disorders of the digestive tract, mainly by means of its carminative and antispasmodic effect. Fennel's great advantage is its pleasant taste and smell. It is also used, but less frequently, in the form of an infusion as an eyewash and in compresses used to heal inflammation of the eyelids, conjunctivitis, styes, etc. The infusion for internal use is prepared from one scant teaspoon of the crushed drug to one cup boiling water sipped slowly three times daily. To young infants it should be given lukewarm by the teaspoonful. In the treatment of digestive disorders the infusion should not be sweetened with sugar whereas in the treatment of inflammation of the upper respiratory passages it is recommended that it be sweetened with honey. The drug is a component of many herbal tea mixtures. It is also used in veterinary medicine. Last but not least, it is still cultivated as a vegetable and condiment in the Mediterranean region, e. g. the varieties *F. vulgare* var. *azoricum* and *F. vulgare* var. *dulce.*

Fennel (1) is a biennial herb reaching up to two metres in height, with smooth, finely furrowed stems and finely divided feathery leaves with thread-like lobes.

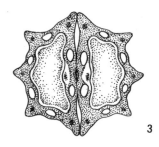

3

The small yellow flowers occur in umbrella-shaped arrangements. The petals are shallowly notched and curve upward. The fruit is a longish ovoid, yellowish, double achene with darker longitudinal ribs. It divides from the base into two achenes with five sharply pronounced ribs (2). The ribs are clearly evident in the cross-section of the achene (3). The ribs contain conductive tissue and in the hollows between the ribs are ducts containing essential oil. Fennel flowers from July till September and ripens with certainty only in warmer localities. That is why in submontane and mountain districts people used to grow the related *Myrrhis odorata* with an essential oil of similar composition and like uses.

1

2

105

Wild Strawberry
Fragaria vesca L.

Rosaceae

The genus *Fragaria* includes some thirty species found in the northern hemisphere in the temperate and subtropical regions as well as in the Andes. Wild Strawberry is native to the temperate regions of Europe and Asia as far as Lake Baikal; in East Asia and North America it is a naturalized species. The parts used medicinally are the leaves together with the stalks. They contain approximately 5 percent tannins, flavonoids and traces of an essential oil. Because of the relatively small percentages of these substances contained in the drug, no pronounced effect is expected, merely a mild astringent, diuretic and antiseptic action, and that is why it was always more or less a neutral component of herbal tea mixtures. However, it enhances the aroma and taste of any tea mixture to which it is added and has no undesirable side effects. The drug by itself is used to treat digestive disorders and urinary infections in the form of an infusion (one teaspoon of the drug to one cup boiling water taken several times daily). The infusion is also a refreshing, invigorating tea for convalescents and its taste makes it an acceptable substitute for real tea. It is also recommended as a preventive measure during the season when there is danger of getting the flu. Externally it is used as a mouth-wash in periodontal disease, for besides its healing action it also eliminates bad breath, and also as a bath preparation for treating haemorrhoids. For external use the infusion is prepared from one tablespoon of the drug per quarter litre of boiling water.

3

Wild Strawberry (1) is a small perennial herb growing in open woodlands, woodland clearings and on grassy banks. It has a branched rhizome and rosette of three-parted basal leaves. The flowers, which occur from May till September, are coloured white and grow on five-to twenty-centimetre-long stems. The fruits are minute achenes spread over the surface of the enlarged fleshy, juicy, almost hemispherical receptacle — the familiar strawberry. It is red, sweet, aromatic, and falls readily. It was introduced into cultivation in Europe in

2

the 15th century and the 18th century saw the beginning of the cultivation of the spreading variety *Fragaria vesca* var. *eflagellis* growing in the Alps, where another variety — var. *semperflorens* — was also found. Crossing the two yielded the familiar continually-fruiting strawberries (2). The large-fruited Garden Strawberry (*Fragaria × ananassa*) was developed in Holland (3). Its leaves are not suitable for medicinal purposes and are not collected for the drug market.

1

Downy Hempnettle
Galeopsis segetum Neck.

Labiatae

The Eurasian genus *Galeopsis* numbers some ten species. Downy Hempnettle is indigenous to western Europe, its range of distribution extending to Denmark and south to northeastern Italy. Elsewhere it is an introduced plant. The flowering stems, but not the woody bottom parts or the fruits, are used medicinally. Because they readily become spoiled by overheating they must be dried as soon as possible after they have been collected. They are gathered mainly in the wild but the plant is also beginning to be cultivated. This is not the only species collected for the drug market. Others that yield the same constituents are Common Hempnettle (*Galeopsis tetrahit*) and *Galeopsis ladanum*. The constituents include soluble silicic acid, saponins and tannins, ancillary sugars and organic acids. In folk medicine the drug is therefore recommended for treating catarrh and virus infections of the upper respiratory passages, bronchitis, tracheitis, laryngitis and pharyngitis, and it continues to be used also for treating coughs in tuberculosis and silicosis. At one time it was used, along with horsetail and knotgrass, as an ingredient of so-called 'Liberian aromatic herbs', a herbal tea mixture used to treat tuberculosis. Downy Hempnettle is also often administered as a mixture in combination with other diuretic drugs. For this purpose the drug by itself is used in the form of a decoction prepared from one teaspoon of the crushed drug to one cup water and taken three times daily. Because of the greater concentration of silicic acid a decoction, i.e. boiling the drug, is preferable to merely pouring boiling water over it. Downy Hempnettle remains a plant whose medicinal properties have not been sufficiently investigated as yet.

Downy Hempnettle (1) is an annual herb with a thin, four-angled, usually branched stem reaching a height of twenty to fifty centimetres. It grows in open woods, woodland clearings, fallow land and field margins in warmer regions. The stem is bristly, mainly on the plump nodes. The leaves are spear-shaped, opposite each other, but each pair is at right angles to those above and below it, with a toothed margin; the blade is often glandular but unlike most members of this family the glands do not contain an essential oil. The flowers, appearing from July until September, are arranged in clusters of six to sixteen, growing from the axils of the upper leaves. The structure of the flower is the same as that of Deadnettle

The corolla is coloured sulphur-yellow
and there is usually a violet pattern on
the upper helmet-shaped lip. The lower
lip has two hollow, tooth-like
appendages (2). The fruit consists of
four ovoid, brownish nutlets.

109

Sweet Woodruff
Galium odoratum (L.) Scop.

Rubiaceae

The Madder family numbers seven thousand species found mainly in the tropics. Sweet Woodruff, however, is native to the temperate regions and subtropical mountains of Eurasia. In North America it is naturalized. The flowering, richly leaved stems are collected in the wild. Care must be taken that they are not damaged as they readily become spoiled by overheating and turn black. The constituents include coumarin, with its characteristic aroma, which is obtained during the drying process from the glycoside melilotosid, aucubin-like aglycone and speruglin and ancillary substances. The drug has antispasmodic and sedative properties. In larger doses, however, the coumarin has a narcotic effect and so is potentially dangerous. The joining of two coumarin molecules gives rise to dicoumarol which effectively prevents blood clotting and thereby the formation of thrombi. That is why in the treatment of varicose veins and thrombophlebitis Sweet Woodruff can be used with success the same as other plants containing coumarin, for example, melilot, rue and knotgrass. In folk medicine it is used primarily to treat general nervous irritability, insomnia and digestive disorders of nervous origin and is also recommended as a mild diuretic for persons with high blood pressure. The drug is administered in the form of an infusion (one teaspoon of the crushed drug to one cup boiling water taken in small drafts two to three times daily). Flavouring foodstuffs with coumarin is advised against because of its pronounced physiological properties. The one exception is the German 'Maibowle' which is prepared by steeping the young shoots in white Rhine wine.

4

Sweet Woodruff (1), a ten- to forty-centimetre-high perennial herb, is a common plant occurring in beech woods from lowland to mountain elevations. The stem is erect and four-angled, terminating in a richly branched arrangement of small white flowers (2). The leaves and stipules are arranged in whorls of as many as eight. After the flowers have faded they are replaced by leathery double achenes (3) which divide into two semi-globe-shaped achenes when ripe. Oil from the seeds of *Dipteryx odorata* (Aubl.) Willd. of the Leguminosae family is also a rich source of coumarin. This plant grows in Brazil, Venezuela and Guyana and its fruits (4) are used to perfume tobacco and cosmetic preparations, as a substitute for vanilla, and as a raw material source of coumarin.

WARNING: Large quantities of this
drug can produce dizziness and
symptoms of poisoning.

111

Licorice
Glycyrrhiza glabra L.

Leguminosae

The genus *Glycyrrhiza* is made up of only fifteen species. The most well known of these is Licorice, native to the Mediterranean region, southeastern Europe and central Asia. The root is used medicinally, and is collected both in the wild and from cultivated plants. It contains numerous saponins, or rather their acids; most highly prized is glycyrrhizin and its aglycone glycyrrhetin. Further constituents include flavonoid glycosides, oxycoumarins and ancillary substances. The drug has a good expectorant action in inflammation of the upper respiratory passages, also mild laxative and antispasmodic properties. It is used in the form of an infusion or briefly boiled decoction (one teaspoon of the finely crushed drug to one cup water), the dosage being one cup three times daily. Used far more frequently, however, is the commercially prepared extract obtained by steeping the drug in warm water (40 °C) and evaporated in a vacuum. It can be obtained in solid or liquid form, depending on the use for which it is intended. It contains 9 to 12 percent glycyrrhizinic acid, whose concentration is the determining factor in the newly propagated treatment of peptic and duodenal ulcers. A number of commercial pharmaceutical preparations are based on this active principle. Despite certain side effects, which are described below, this treatment continues to be recommended. The method is to dissolve 20 g of the solid extract in a glass of chamomile tea which is drunk in one day in small amounts after meals for a period of about three days. In many instances this 'cure' proves successful. Licorice is not a dangerous drug. However the dosage cannot be arbitrarily increased nor used for long periods.

Licorice (1) is a large, perennial herb reaching a height of one and a half metres, with a woody root and cylindrical stolons (2). The stems are erect and branched, the leaves odd-pinnate, with five to seven pairs of leaflets that are slightly sticky on the underside due to the resin glands. The flowers, arranged similarly to hyacinths or Lily of the valley, appear in July and August. The typically-shaped corolla is coloured various shades of violet-blue. The fruit is a pod containing between one and four globe-shaped seeds. The roots of Licorice vary in size depending on the plant's age; those of old specimens are tough and difficult to process. They are called 'sweet wood' and are also used in the food industry to flavour cakes, sweets, drinks, and other items.

WARNING: Licorice may increase fluid
retention and blood pressure, therefore
it must not be used in cases of
hypertension. Blood pressure must in
any case be monitored. There is also
a threat to blood potassium levels and
therefore it should not be used in
conjunction with Digitalis drugs.

1

2

113

Smooth Rupturewort
Herniaria glabra L.

Caryophyllaceae

The genus *Herniaria,* numbering twenty species, is indigenous to Europe, western Asia and north Africa. This applies also to the distribution of the two species used medicinally—Smooth Rupturewort and the more warmth-loving Hairy Rupturewort (*H. hirsuta*). The flowering stems devoid of the roots are used to produce the drug. They are yellow-green, odourless (Smooth Rupturewort) or with a faint coumarin scent (Hairy Rupturewort), slightly bitter and cause a scratchy sensation on the tongue. The drug contains saponins, coumarin derivatives such as herniarin, flavonoid glycosides, and other ancillary substances. It has a diuretic, antispasmodic and antiseptic effect in inflammation of the urinary passages and ensuing painful spasms of the bladder and urinary passages and is given in the form of an infusion steeped briefly or for several hours (one teaspoon of the crushed drug to one cup water taken three to four times daily in small drafts). According to R. F. Weiss fresh stems steeped for a long period have a more effective antispasmodic action than the steeped drug because the antispasmodic properties are purportedly lost by drying. In view of the relative abundance of this plant in Europe and Asia it is possible to use the fresh stems during the growing period, otherwise there is no alternative than to use the crude drug. If the stems are properly collected at the beginning of the flowering period and dried by natural heat, such a carefully obtained drug can fully take the place of fresh stems. Smooth Rupturewort derives its name from the oldest purpose for which it was used in folk medicine—namely to treat bowel problems associated with hernias. It is still an important diuretic drug.

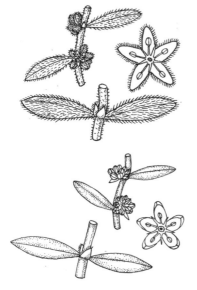

Smooth Rupturewort (1) is a small yellow-green herb with mat-forming, branched, densely leaved, prostrate stems spreading out in a circle. The taproot provides this plant of trampled places, paved paths, dikes, sandy places, etc. with an adequate supply of water. The opposite leaves appear to be alternate because one is always rudimentary (enlarged plant—2). The flowers are arranged in clusters, about ten to a cluster. They are minute, five-petalled, greenish, with loose involucres and measuring about one millimetre in diameter. The flowering period is from July till September; the fruit is a one-seeded nutlet. Hairy Rupturewort (3), less common than

114

2

1

Smooth Rupturewort (4), is
distinguishable by its grey-green colour,
produced by the hairiness of the entire
plant. The differences between the two
species are most clearly evident in the
leaves and calyxes.

Sea Buckthorn
Hippophaë rhamnoides L.   Elaegnaceae

The genus *Hippophaë* has only a single species comprising several subspecies distributed in the temperate regions of Eurasia. In Europe it grows wild, for instance, in the Alps, Pyrenees and Caucasus and the respective piedmont regions on river gravel. It also grows on the coastal dunes of the North and Baltic Seas. Another small species — *H. salicifolia* D. Don is found in the Himalayas. Because the concentration of vitamin C in the berries of Sea Buckthorn averages as much as 1,400 mg the shrub began to be cultivated on plantations for its fruit. It also contains smaller quantities of vitamins A, B, E and P. The berries furthermore have a balanced proportion of organic acids and sugars, pectin and essential oil, giving the pulp a pleasant and rather unusual aroma. The fruits are gathered when they begin to ripen, when the berries turn orange and are not yet soft. Only the freshly pressed juice from the berries is used as such or made into syrups or preserves. Because of the high vitamin C content these products are also important from the viewpoint of health. Unlike the tasteless commercial vitamin preparations they enliven the vitamin diet with their flavour and aroma and are also a recommended part of the diet during convalescence, to counteract general weakness and fatigue, and as protection against possible infection, particularly in late winter and early spring.

2 ♂

3 ♀

Sea Buckthorn (1) is a shrub which reaches two metres in height, with a spreading root system and much-branched, thorny, silvery-grey twigs. The leaves are alternate, narrow spears very thinly covered in hairs above and scaly silvery-grey on the underside. The flowers appear before the leaves in April and May. The male and female flowers are borne on separate bushes and on plantations it is therefore necessary to have several male bushes that do not bear fruits. The flowers are inconspicuous and of simple structure.

The male flowers (2) are in globe-shaped axillary clusters, the female flowers (3) in short dense hyacinth-like bunches. The fruits are juicy, densely clustered, orange berries 9 millimetres in diameter and are gathered in August and September. For purposes of large-scale cultivation on plantations, mainly in the USSR, selective breeding focuses on producing plants without thorns and with larger fruits. Sea Buckthorn is also popular as an undemanding park and garden ornamental, for its foliage and fruits.

117

Hop, Hops
Humulus lupulus L.   Canabaceae

Hop is a climbing herb found in the temperate regions of Eurasia, growing wild mainly around the fiftieth parallel. Only plants grown in cultivation in central and southern Europe and the warmer regions of Asia and North America as well as Australia are used for pharmaceutical purposes and in the food industry. The cultivation of Hops in Europe dates from early medieval days, in France probably since the middle of the 8th century. In Germany and Bohemia it has been grown since the 14th century, exclusively as a bitter substance for the brewing of beer. Its medicinal properties were not discovered until later. The parts collected for the drug are the strobiles or merely the glands on the surface of the bracts that form the strobiles. The strobiles contain lupulin, bitter resinous substances and an essential oil, the glands are a kind of concentrated form of the active principles, containing as much as 3 percent essential oil and 80 percent bitter resins (humulone, lupulone, etc.). These substances give the drug sedative, hypnotic and stomachic properties and also lower the male sex drive. For relieving anxiety and tension and inducing sleep it is recommended to take the drug in the form of an infusion, one tablespoon of the crushed strobiles to one cup water, before bedtime. To relieve digestive disorders increase the dose to one cup of the infusion three times daily after meals. In the case of glands, the amount for a single dose is 1 g, i.e. less than a full teaspoon, washed down by a cup of any kind of tea. This, too, is taken at bedtime for insomnia, or three times daily for digestive disorders.

2

Wild Hop (1) grows fairly freely in alder groves and coastal thickets. It is a climbing herb with roughly hooked hairy stems that twine in a clockwise direction. The leaves are opposite and resemble those of the grapevine. There are both male and female plants but only the female plants are cultivated in hop-fields, in many different varieties. The female flowers are clustered in cone-like strobiles, two to three centimetres long, coloured green at first, later turning yellow as they ripen (2). The bracts are thickly covered with glands, whose structure is evident in the enlarged drawing (3). The active principles also have excellent cosmetic properties able to curb 'aging' of the complexion and brittleness of the hair. As far back as the Middle Ages bath attendants added hops or brewery sediment to rejuvenating baths and treated hair with beer. Modern-day

cosmetics utilize this age-old knowledge
and experience albeit in a different
form.

WARNING: The use of hops in
individual suffering from depressive
illnesses should be avoided.

119

Perforate St. John's Wort,
Common St. John's Wort
Hypericum perforatum L.

Hypericaceae

The genus *Hypericum* has a great many species, most of them found in the subtropical regions. Perforate St. John's Wort is an exception. It is distributed throughout most of Europe, western and central Asia to the Altai and the Himalayas in the south, and has become naturalized on all the continents. The flowering top parts devoid of the lower, leafless, woody parts of the stems are gathered at the beginning of the flowering period. They contain dianthrones, e.g. hypericin, the flavonoid glycoside hyperosid, an essential oil, catechol tannins and ancillary substances. The drug is used to treat a number of ailments, first and foremost depression, melancholia, disturbed sleep due to anxiety or tension and bed-wetting as well as digestive disorders, mainly of nervous origin, starting with gall bladder disorders and upset stomach. It is also used externally for its antiseptic and healing properties to treat wounds, varicose ulcers, phlebitis, etc. The drug is used in the form of an infusion, one to two teaspoons of the crushed drug to one cup boiling water—one to two cups taken daily every morning and evening, or in the form of an extract, ten drops three times daily. Marked results cannot be expected for at least one month, particularly in the case of nervous diseases. Suitable for external use is an extract made from the crushed fresh flowers which are treated with olive or some other oil that does not turn rancid. The flowers are macerated in oil for two months, after which they are exposed to the sun and, when they have turned red, the mixture is filtered through cotton to separate the residue and applied to wounds and inflamed areas.

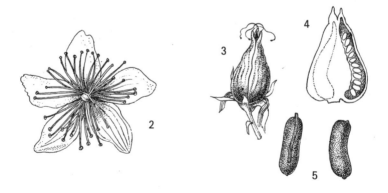

120

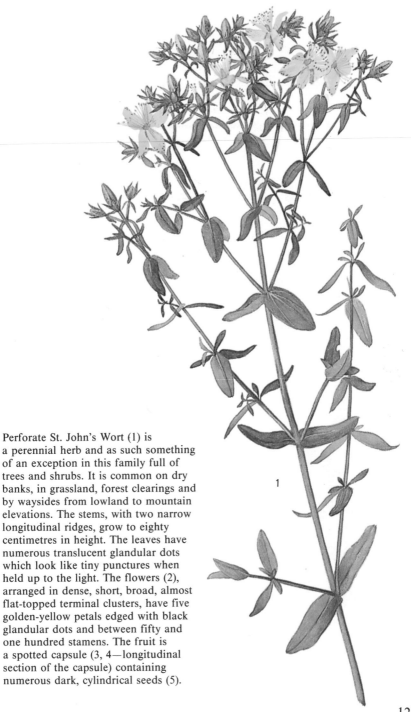

Perforate St. John's Wort (1) is
a perennial herb and as such something
of an exception in this family full of
trees and shrubs. It is common on dry
banks, in grassland, forest clearings and
by waysides from lowland to mountain
elevations. The stems, with two narrow
longitudinal ridges, grow to eighty
centimetres in height. The leaves have
numerous translucent glandular dots
which look like tiny punctures when
held up to the light. The flowers (2),
arranged in dense, short, broad, almost
flat-topped terminal clusters, have five
golden-yellow petals edged with black
glandular dots and between fifty and
one hundred stamens. The fruit is
a spotted capsule (3, 4—longitudinal
section of the capsule) containing
numerous dark, cylindrical seeds (5).

Elecampane
Inula helenium L. Compositae

The genus *Inula,* comprising one hundred species, is distributed in Eurasia and Africa. Elecampane is indigenous to central Asia and has been cultivated since ancient times becoming naturalized as a garden escape in many places. Used medicinally are the rhizomes and roots of second-year plants and are obtained almost exclusively through cultivation. The constituents include mainly an essential oil with azulene and sesquiterpenic lactones, formerly collectively termed helenin or so-called *Elecampane camphor.* The drug also contains triterpenic compounds, bitter principles, and up to 40 percent inulin. It is used primarily for coughs, bronchitis and emphysema. The drug is also a component of many herbal teas used for coughs and the extract from the drug is included in pills used for the same purpose. Elecampane also has antispasmodic properties, stimulates the flow of bile and has a beneficial effect on the digestion, facts well known in folk medicine. One teaspoon of the crushed drug is boiled briefly in one cup water and the decoction is then sipped slowly — three cups daily. The high concentration of inulin is the reason for the drug's marginal use for diabetes. Elecampane has been used medicinally for thousands of years, the first written mention of the herb appearing in the *Codex Constantinopolitanus* dating from 512 A. D. The drug is also used to a limited degree in the food and cosmetics industries.

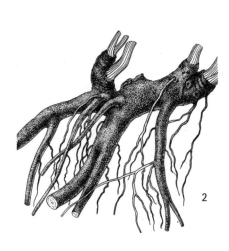

Elecampane (1) is a robust perennial herb with a large, branched, tuberous root. The stem, growing to a height of a metre and a half, is erect, thick, softly hairy to felted, and branched at the top (2). The leaves are grey-felted on the underside; the ones at the base are stalked and arranged in a rosette, those on the stem are sessile. The large terminal flowerheads open in July and August. They have a flat receptacle and semiglobose involucre composed of several rows of densely overlapping bracts. The flowers are yellow. The striking tongue-shaped flowers on the margin have a very short tube and narrow tongue tipped with several 'teeth'. The dics flowers are five-petalled and tubular with funnel-shaped corolla. The fruit is a rounded, hairless, longitudinaly ribbed achene with a long pappus on the top. Elecampane is also grown as an ornamental plant and occasionally occurs as a garden escape.

1

Common Juniper
Juniperus communis L.

Cupressaceae

Like all the other sixty species belonging to this genus, Common Juniper is distributed throughout the northern hemisphere in Europe, Asia and North America from the southern edge of the Arctic southward to the Atlas Mountains, the Caucasus and the Himalayas. The ripe fruits, juniper berries, are used medicinally. They contain a component-rich, aromatic essential oil (about 1 percent) similar to turpentine oil. Other constituents include flavonoids, tannins and ancillary substances, including about 3 percent invert sugar. This drug is the most widely used diuretic agent for diseases of the urinary tract, and dropsy. It is used in the form of an infusion: one teaspoon of the drug crushed just before use to one cup boiling water taken in the morning and evening. Common Juniper is also used to treat digestive disorders, where it stimulates the flow of bile and improves the appetite. Otherwise healthy people can benefit from drinking distilled juniper liquor. The drug is also used, although less commonly, to treat diseases associated with chilling, such as the common cold. Externally, the drug is used in the treatment of muscular rheumatism, sore tendons, stiff muscles, etc. in the form of an infusion, one cup taken three times daily as well as an alcohol extract from the berries applied as a rub or added to the bath.

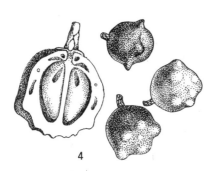

2

3

4

Common Juniper (1) is a coniferous evergreen shrub or many-branched small tree. It takes the form of undergrowth in open woods, on grasslands, heaths and moors from lowland to mountain elevations. Male plants are of conical habit, female plants are of spreading habit. The leaves are needle-like, sharply spiny, and with a duct containing essential oil inside. The fruits (2), borne on female plants, take two to three years to ripen. They are green at first, then blue-black when ripe, and contain one to three elongate, angular, pale brown seeds with hard seed coat (3 — cross-section of berry).

WARNING: It is possible to mistake the berries of Sabin (*Juniperus sabina* L.) for Common Juniper berries. **Sabin berries are poisonous;** like all parts of the plant they contain the toxin sabinol. The two species can be readily distinguished by the difference in the shape of the berries (4). Common Juniper should not be taken for a period exceeding five weeks because elimination of albumin in the urine may occur along with kidney disorders. Similarly it must not be taken during pregnancy or when the kidneys are inflamed.

1

White Deadnettle, Archangel
Lamium album L.
Labiatae

The genus *Lamium* numbers some forty species native to Europe, North Africa and non-tropical regions of Asia. White Deadnettle is the type species. It is indigenous to the temperate regions of Eurasia. The corollas and stamens of the flowers, but not the calyxes, are used medicinally. They are obtained solely by collecting in the wild, a very laborious process. The gathered flowers must not be crumpled, packed tight, and hence become overheated, for they readily turn brown, thereby losing their attractive appearance, aroma and taste, as well as potency. The drug contains biogenic amines, flavonoid glycosides, mucilage, organic acids, catechol tannins and traces of an essential oil. It has a wide range of uses in folk medicine: for 'purifying the blood' in the form of tea, for diseases of the upper respiratory tract, digestive disorders, nervous depression, and because of its mild diuretic and antiseptic properties also for inflammation of the kidneys, urinary tract and prostate gland. It is taken in the form of an infusion, the usual dose being one teaspoon of the drug to one cup water taken as often as five times daily. Equally important is the use of the infusion externally, one tablespoon of the drug to one litre of previously boiled water, as a douche for vaginal discharge, coupled with taking it internally, also in healing compresses for wounds, ulcers and skin rashes. The tender young, non-flowering plants are popularly eaten in spring soups and salads.

White Deadnettle (1) is a perennial weedy species of herb growing in thickets, at the edges of woods, by waysides, and in waste places from lowland to mountain elevations. It has a creeping, many-branched rhizome and rooting runners. The stems, bearing pairs of leaves growing at right angles to those above and below them, are four-angled and twenty to forty centimetres high. The flowers, borne from June until October, are arranged in loose whorls, ten or more to a whorl, growing from the upper leaf joints. The honey-scented flowers are symmetrical with bell-shaped calyx and two-lipped, white corolla, the upper lip distinctly forming a hood. The anthers in front are longer than the ones at the back. The fruit consists of four triangular nutlets.

1

The species *Lamium purpureum* (2) has the same properties as White Deadnettle but is not suitable for the drug market because its purplish-red corollas either turn a dark or pale faded hue when dried which makes their appearance unappealing, even for use in herbal tea mixtures.

Garden Lavender
Lavandula angustifolia Mill.

Labiatae

The genus *Lavandula* with its twenty-eight species of herbs, subshrubs and shrubs, is native to the area extending from the Canary Islands through the Mediterranean region to Somalia, India and Pakistan. Garden Lavender is native to the Mediterranean region from Spain to Yugoslavia but is widely grown elsewhere as well, mainly for its essential oil, used in perfumes and cosmetics. The flowering, leafy stems or the flowers alone are used medicinally. The constituents include an essential oil, up to 3 percent, with linalool and numerous other components, also other substances with therapeutic properties — coumarin, umbeliferon and tannins. The drug has a mild sedative action on the central nervous system and slightly lowers high blood pressure; it has a lesser effect in gall bladder and bile duct disorders. It is used in the form of an infusion made by adding one teaspoon of the drug to one cup boiling water and taken in the morning and evening, or alcohol extract, twenty to thirty drops per dose. The drug also has a sedative effect in the form of baths which are recommended for neuroses during menopause and for disorders of muscle tone governed by the action of the sympathetic and parasympathetic nervous system. For this purpose an infusion is prepared from three to four tablespoons of the drug from flowers or six to eight tablespoons of the drug from the flowering stems per one litre of water. In folk medicine the drug is a popular remedy for digestive disorders and as a mild diuretic. The alcohol extract may be used externally to cause mild inflammation of the skin in the treatment of rheumatic and sciatic pains.

2

Garden Lavender (1) is a twenty- to thirty-centimetre-high, grey-green felted subshrub with narrow leaves which grow opposite each other, each pair at right angles to those above and below it. It is a natural component of the communities of plants adapted to the very dry conditions of the Mediterranean region. In Europe it has been cultivated for its oil since the 16th century. The flowers (2), arranged in loose, spike-like sprays, have a tubular, grey-violet calyx with numerous glandular hairs filled with essential oil and are apparent from June until August. The corolla is violet, and the pair of stamens in front is longer than those at the back. The fruit consists of four smooth, glossy nutlets (3 — view from either side). Other species of the genus, mainly Spike Lavender (*L. latifolia*), are more important for

3

their commercial rather than medicinal value. The most widely cultivated for their remarkable yield of lavender oil, as much as three hundred tons annually worldwide, are hybrids of the two aforesaid species classified as *Lavandula × intermedia.*

1

Motherwort
Leonurus cardiaca L.

Labiatae

The genus *Leonorus*, numbering nine species, is native to Europe and central Asia. Motherwort is most likely indigenous to western Asia. It spread as a garden escape and has become naturalized throughout Europe to such a degree that it appears to be indigenous. This was due in great part to its being widely cultivated for medicinal purposes in former times. Nowadays demand for the drug is relatively small, hence the plant's cultivation is likewise limited. The densely leaved flowering stems, devoid of the thick, bare, woody lower parts, are used medicinally. They contain glycosides that have a mild cardiotonic and diuretic action, bitter principles, traces of an essential oil and a small amount of alkaloids. It is recommended as a mild heart stimulant in neuroses of the autonomic nervous system, for the treatment of prostate problems and as a sedative, in the form of an infusion, one teaspoon of the cut drug to one cup boiling water taken two to three times daily. Drinking the infusion is particularly effective for the elderly heart because it improves the heart rate, and is also effective in the early stages of prostate problems. It can be used as a sedative during menopause and for suppressing unpleasant symptoms caused by an enlarged thyroid gland. In substance the effects of the drug are those of a geriatric medicament, i. e. one that suppresses the pathological manifestations of the aging organism. Motherwort has been used to treat heart diseases most probably since the Middle Ages.

Motherwort (1) is a relatively large perennial herb, which grows to a height of one hundred and twenty centimetres. It has an erect, many-branched, square, hollow stem and leaves which grow opposite each other at right angles to the pair above and below it, that are irregularly toothed and have prominent veins on the underside; they are five- to seven-lobed on the lower part of the stem, and three-lobed towards the top. It is a plant of grasslands, village greens, waste places and waysides, found in warmer districts from lowland to hilly country. The flowers, which are present from June till September (2), grow in whorls of ten to twenty in the middle and upper leaf joints, and are sessile and symmetrical with a bell-shaped calyx containing five awn-like teeth. The corolla is two-lipped, generally pale pink, very occasionally white, the upper lip brownish-hairy, the lower lip shorter and with brownish-red spots on the lobes; the stamens have outspread pollen sacs. The fruit consists of four nutlets that fall together with the calyx when ripe.

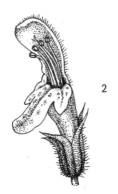

2

1

Lovage
Levisticum officinale W. D. J. Koch

Umbelliferae

Lovage is the most familiar of the three species of *Levisticum*. Nowadays it is known only as a cultivated plant found on all the continents. In all probability it is descended from the species *Levisticum persicum* which grows wild in southern Iran. The rhizome and roots are used medicinally; they contain an essential oil with phthalic acid lactones and other components, furocoumarins, and ancillary substances. These constituents give the drug marked diuretic properties and curb flatulence. The drug is used for inflammation of the urinary passages and bladder in the form of an infusion steeped either briefly or for a lengthier period. In the first instance one cup of boiling water is poured over one teaspoon of the crushed drug and allowed to stand for ten to twenty minutes, in the second instance tepid water is poured over the drug and left standing for two to three hours; two to three cups of the tea should be drunk during the course of the day. The drug is rarely used by itself; it is generally a component of diuretic herbal tea mixtures. It may be prepared in the same way as stated above for treating digestive disorders in that it improves digestion, stimulates the flow of digestive secretions, relieves flatulence and improves the appetite. Lovage is an excellent flavouring agent and potherb and has been used as such for many years. Foods prepared with Lovage are tasty and more digestible. The leaves or the ground fruits rather than the root are used for this purpose. They have a lower concentration of aromatic substances and are therefore more suitable for use in foods. Lovage is also used in the pharmaceutical industry. It is an ancient medicinal herb, often referred to by herbalists across the ages.

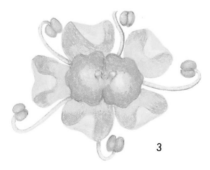

3

Lovage is a perennial herb with a fleshy overwintering rhizome and erect, hollow stems up to one and half metres high terminated by the flowerhead (1, 2). The leaves are alternate, the lower ones long-stalked, those higher up either short-stalked or with sheath-like stalks; they are two or three times pinnate, the upper stem leaves less divided. The flowers appear from June until August and are arranged in clusters of as many as twenty umbels. The small five-petalled flowers (3) are greenish-yellow. The fruit is

a yellow-brown, ellipsoid, double achene
flattened on the back which divides
lengthwise from the bottom into two
five-ribbed achenes when ripe. The
schematic cross-section (4) clearly shows
low wings on the three middle ribs and
broader wings on the marginal ribs. In
the hollows between the ribs there are
ducts containing essential oil and the
ribs themselves are composed of
conductive tissue.

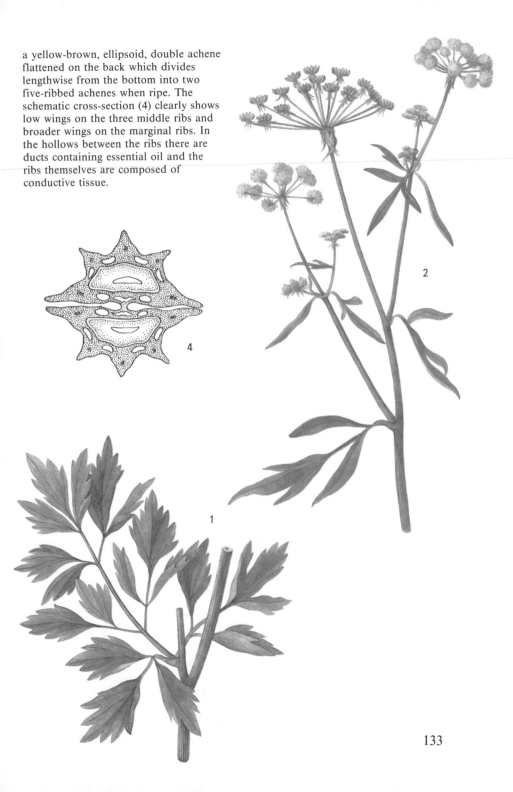

Common Toadflax
Linaria vulgaris MILL.

Scrophulariaceae

The genus *Linaria* numbers some one hundred and fifty species distributed throughout the northern hemisphere, whose centre of origin lies in the Mediterranean region. The illustrated species is native to central Europe, its range extending to western Asia, and has become naturalized in North America. The flowering stems are gathered from June until September, being cut off about twenty centimetres above the ground before the flowers have passed their prime. They contain bitter flavonoid glycosides (e. g. linarin), tannins, and the alkaloid peganin, better known as a constituent of the species *Peganum harmala* giving Common Toadflax anti-inflammatory, diuretic and laxative properties. The drug is administered in the form of an infusion, one teaspoon of the crumbled drug to one cup boiling water, two to four cups daily, for prostate problems and difficulty in urinating. It can also be used in the form of an alcohol extract, thirty drops three times daily, which is purportedly more effective than the infusion in the case of prostate trouble. The infusion from the drug softens the stool and helps renew peristalsis. One of the possible side-effects of drinking the infusion may be mild spasms caused by the alkaloid peganin, but these are not dangerous. Externally, phlebitis, varicose ulcers, haemorrhoids, and skin rashes are treated with a bath (an infusion prepared from two tablespoons of the drug per half litre of water) or a mushy compress (20 g of the drug boiled in half a litre of milk). The haemorrhoid ointment with Toadflax as its main component (*Unguentum linariae*) was created by the Hessen physician Johann Wolpius.

Common Toadflax (1) is a weedy perennial herb with a creeping rhizome and a stem reaching a height of fifty centimetres. It grows in dry places — by

railway tracks, fields, walls, hedges and on waste ground, from lowland to mountain elevations. The smooth, simple stem with alternate linear leaves resembling those of flax (hence the plant's name) is terminated by a dense hyacinth-like flowerhead from June until September. The flowers are symmetrical (2); the two-lipped corolla is yellow with an orange spot at the throat and a long pointed spur at the base. This species is an example of peloria, i. e. the abnormal formation of a regular flower instead of a symmetrical flower at the tip of the flowerhead. The fruit is an ovoid, two-chambered capsule containing winged seeds and is longer than the persistent calyx.

White Horehound
Marrubium vulgare L. Labiatae

The genus *Marrubium* numbers thirty species. White Horehound grows throughout Europe and western Asia in temperate and subtropical regions. It is native to the Mediterranean region, elsewhere it is merely naturalized. Because collecting in the wild often does not meet the demand for the drug, specially bred varieties with high yields are cultivated commercially. The upper stems which contain bitter principles (marrubiin), flavonoids, tannins, mucilage, organic acids and a slight quantity of an essential oil with a strong apple-like fragrance are gathered at the beginning of the flowering period. White Horehound is used for mild digestive disorders accompanied by loss of appetite and diarrhoea. It stimulates the flow of bile and the flavonoid-tannin component has an anti-inflammatory and antiseptic effect. In folk medicine the drug is also used for inflammation of the upper respiratory passages, but it is not as effective as other drugs. In combination with Hawthorn leaves it can be used to treat heart rhythm irregularities of nervous origin and brewed with Balm and Lavender it makes a pleasant-tasting tea that calms the nerves. The infusion is prepared from one tablespoon of the drug to one cup water sipped unsweetened in small drafts, with a dosage of two to three cups daily. When used in an herbal mixture the dosage is the same. The closely related *M. peregrinum* or hybrids of the two may also be used as a remedy.

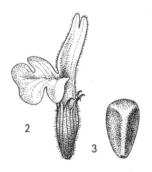

White Horehound (1) is a perennial herb which reaches a height of half a metre being coloured whitish and woolly at first, becoming downy later. The stem is four-angled, hollow and branched. The leaves are opposite, growing at right angles to those above and below, and wrinkled. It grows in sunny, nutrient-rich locations, often waste places; it requires a great deal of warmth and light as well as nitrogen-rich soil and flowers from June until September. The dense whorls of as many as eight flowers grow from the leaf joints in the upper third of the stem. The flowers (2) have a divided tubular calyx with hooked teeth. The corolla is two-lipped, downy and white; the lower lip has a long central lobe. The two stamens in front are longer than the ones at the back. Four ovoid, three-angled nutlets (3) make up the fruit falling together with the calyx when ripe.

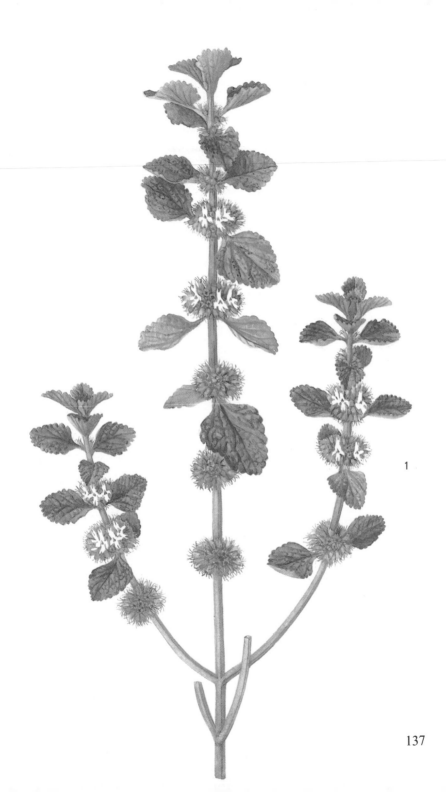

1

137

Balm, Lemon Balm, Bee Balm
Melissa officinalis L.　　　　　　　　　　　　　　Labiatae

Balm was introduced into cultivation in Spain in the 7th century by Arabs and has been grown elsewhere in the Mediterranean region since ancient times. It probably became naturalized there because two other species of the genus are native to the region from the Himalayas eastward. The leaves were always the parts used medicinally in former times; nowadays the flowering top parts devoid of the lower, leafless, woody parts of the stems are gathered. They contain a citral-type essential oil, bitter principles and flavonoids plus other ancillary substances. One would expect that the low concentration of the essential oil (max. 0.3 percent) would limit the effectiveness of the drug but it has been proven that the low concentration in combination with the other constituents is, in fact, what produces positive results which cannot be improved by increasing the dosage. The drug is used to treat a number of basic conditions. First, it is valued for its calming effect and is recommended for insomnia, digestive disorders, and palpitations of a nervous origin. It is used in the form of an infusion, one tablespoon of the crumbled drug to one cup boiling water to be taken in the morning and at bedtime. Stomach problems, likewise mainly of nervous origin, respond to treatment by Balm, in which case the drug improves digestion by harmonizing the action of the gallbladder and stomach at the same time relieving flatulence. The infusion for treating these conditions is prepared in the same way but the dosage is three to four cups daily. Of the many pharmaceutical preparations containing Balm the most popular is the alcohol extract known as 'Carmelite drops'. Twenty to thirty drops three times daily is the recommended dosage in place of the above infusion.

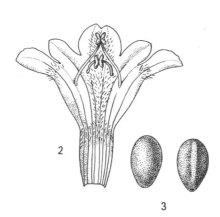

Balm (1) is a perennial herb reaching a height of eighty centimetres. It is known only in cultivation, occasionally occurring as a garden escape. The stems are four-angled and very leafy. The leaves are in pairs opposite each other, each pair being at right angles to those above and below it, coarsely edged with rounded teeth that point forward, hairy, and with glands containing an essential oil with a lemon scent. The small flowers grow in whorls in the upper leaf joints, from May until August. Longitudinal section of the flower (2) showing the tubular bell-like calyx and white, yellowish-white or pink-tinged two-lipped corolla with two stamens longer than the rest. The ovary has a ring at the base that exudes nectar, and later forms a fruit consisting of

138

1

ovoid nutlets (3). Balm is much visited
by bees. It is also used as a culinary
herb and as an aromatic ingredient in
liqueurs.

Peppermint
Mentha × piperita L.

Labiatae

All fifteen species of the genus *Mentha* enjoy worldwide popularity in the treatment of digestive disorders. Most highly valued of the lot is the hybrid Peppermint, whose origins are unknown. It is cultivated on all continents and on a larger scale than any other plant grown for medicinal purposes or for its essential oil. The variety developed in the 18th century in England, in the town of Mitcham in Surrey, is the one preferred for pharmaceutical purposes. Originally only the leaves were intended to be used medicinally but large-scale cultivation of the plant necessitated the use of the top parts as well. Both the leaves and the top parts are gathered at the beginning of the flowering period. They contain 1 to 3 percent of an essential oil, of which menthol is the main component, as well as tannins and bitter principles. These constituents give the drug its antispasmodic and antiseptic properties, soothe the irritated lining of the stomach, relieve flatulence, promote the flow of bile and furthermore make the drug palatable to most patients. Peppermint is commonly used in the treatment of colic, gall bladder pains, painful flatulence, and intestinal problems, and is administered in the form of an infusion — one teaspoon of the drug to one cup water, three cups daily altogether, taken in small drafts always after meals or between the main meals of the day. The essential oil is used widely for flavouring toothpastes and mouthwashes, in refreshing massage creams as well as in ointments and inhalations for colds. Natural menthol is obtained mainly from the essential oil of the east Asian species *Mentha arvensis* L. var. *piperascens,* which contains even more than 80 percent menthol.

Peppermint (1) is a hairless, strongly aromatic perennial herb reaching a height of more than half a metre. The stems grow from a creeping rhizome and form numerous rooting surface runners by means of which the plant spreads, for it is sterile and does not produce seeds. The leaves are in pairs, opposite each other, each pair being at right angles to those above and below it, stalked, and a long oval shape, and it is these that have the greatest number of glands containing the essential oil. The flowers (2), which are present from June until August, are arranged in long terminal spikes, with a pinkish-violet corolla and four protruding stamens of equal length. At the base of the ovary is a nectar-producing ring. Another species used commercially is Spearmint (*Mentha spicata*), native to France, northern Italy and Dalmatia. It is cultivated mainly in North America for use in toothpastes and mouthwashes as well as in the food industry for chewing gum, confectionery and liqueurs.

Buckbean, Bogbean, Marsh Trefoil
Menyanthes trifoliata L.
Menyanthaceae

This, the only species in the genus *Menyanthes*, is native to the temperate regions of the northern hemisphere. Its range extends north to Greenland and Iceland and south to the northwestern coast of Africa, to Transcaucasia, the Himalayas and Yünnan and is also found in the USA and Canada. The leaves (*Folium trifolii fibrini*) with a small bit of the petiole are used but the rhizomes are protected and collecting them is prohibited. When gathering the leaves it is necessary to handle the plants with care and leave a sufficient number of **untouched** specimens at the site. Often it is impossible to meet the demand for the drug by collecting the plant in the wild for it is becoming increasingly rare. It is becoming necessary to consider future cultivation of the herb even though this would be an exacting undertaking from the technical as well as economic aspect. The drug contains glycosidic bitter principles, e.g. loganin, and ancillary substances which determine the drug's use. Buckbean is a classic bitter tonic used for a wide variety of digestive disorders beginning with loss of appetite and also has a good effect in general exhaustion, during convalescence following an infectious disease or operation, when the weakened stomach, in view of its lowered muscle tone, has difficulty coping with food. It is administered in the form of an infusion, one less-than-full teaspoon to one cup water taken three times daily before meals. Some persons do not tolerate the drug by itself and for that reason it is used in combination with other drugs, e.g. Chamomile and Peppermint. It has been used for pharmaceutical purposes since the 17th century and nowadays is an important raw material for the isolation of natural bitter principles.

Buckbean (1) is a water-loving perennial herb, growing mainly by the edges of lakes and ponds, in marshes, bogs, and wet ditches from lowland to mountain elevations. It has a jointed, branched, creeping rhizome which bears fleshy, three-parted leaves with a stalk that widens into a sheath at the base. The erect, leafless stem, up to forty centimetres high, is terminated by a short hyacinth-like flowerhead with as many as twenty flowers, appearing from May until June (2). The flowers are five-petalled and radiate with a calyx which is deeply divided into five lobes, a corolla which is broadly funnel-shaped and divided into five densely fringed lobes coloured pink outside and white

3

inside, and stamens joined to the inside of the corolla tube, as evident in the drawing showing the flower opened out flat (3). The fruit is a thin, dry, membranous capsule with numerous disc-like seeds.

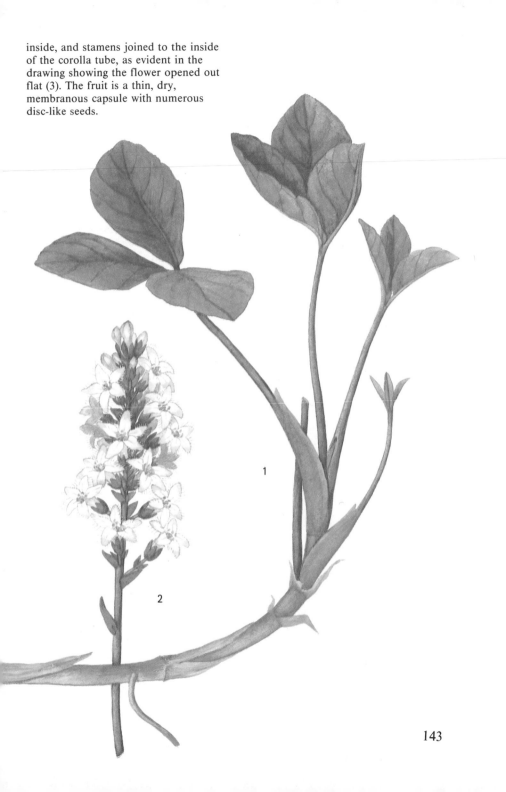

Sweet Basil
Ocimum basilicum L.

The genus *Ocimum*, which is made up of more than sixty species, includes aromatic subshrubs and herbs indigenous to the tropical regions of Africa, Asia and America. Since the days of the Egyptian pharaohs, and perhaps even earlier, Basil has been grown in many countries throughout the world, even in nontropical regions, as an important culinary and medicinal herb and also as food for bees. The leafy stems, cut off without the lower woody part of the stem at the beginning of the flowering period, are used medicinally and are the most important part of the plant in terms of the concentration of essential oil, tannins and ancillary substances. The essential oil contains methylchavicol as the main component. The drug has a beneficial effect on the digestive system in that it stimulates the flow of bile, improves digestion and relieves flatulence and painful spasms in poor digestion. In folk medicine it is noted for its calming effect, this being apparently due to its beneficial action on digestion which results in the contentment and calmness of the person involved. The drug has a very agreeable flavour as well as fragrance. It is used in the form of an infusion, one teaspoon of the crumbled drug to one cup boiling water sipped slowly after meals or between the main meals with a dosage of two to three cups daily. During the growing period fresh leaves may be used instead of dried leaves. Basil is a popular culinary herb, particularly in Italian cookery.

Sweet Basil (1) is a cultivated annual herb reaching a height of forty centimetres with a many-branched reddish stem. All parts of the plant are hairy and have a distinctive aroma. The short-stalked leaves are in pairs opposite each other, growing at right angles to those above and below it, and reddish in colour. The flowering period is from June until September. The spike-like flowerhead is composed of pseudowhorls of six two-lipped flowers each (2). The corolla is yellowish-white, occasionally pink or even red; the tube is short, the upper lip four-lobed, the

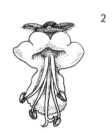

2

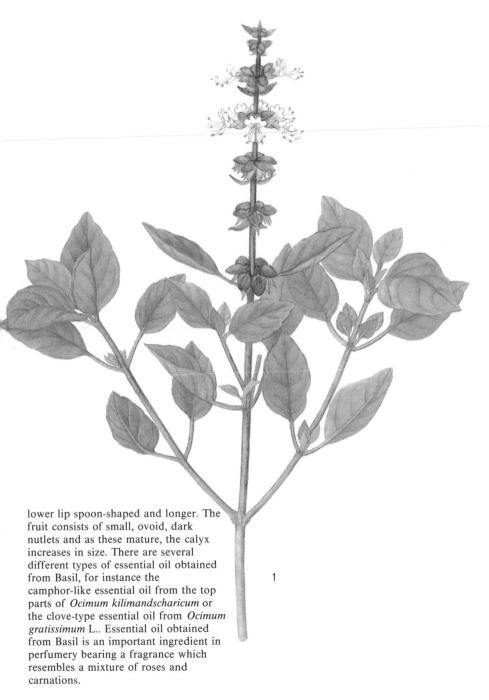

lower lip spoon-shaped and longer. The fruit consists of small, ovoid, dark nutlets and as these mature, the calyx increases in size. There are several different types of essential oil obtained from Basil, for instance the camphor-like essential oil from the top parts of *Ocimum kilimandscharicum* or the clove-type essential oil from *Ocimum gratissimum* L.. Essential oil obtained from Basil is an important ingredient in perfumery bearing a fragrance which resembles a mixture of roses and carnations.

1

Spiny Restharrow
Ononis spinosa L.

Leguminosae

Some seventy species of the genus *Ononis* have been described to date, their centre of origin being located in the Mediterranean region. The species illustrated here belongs to the flora of central Europe but is also found in western Asia eastward to Turkestan. The part used medicinally is the root whose constituents include glycosidic iso-flavonoids and their aglycones formononetin and onogenin, the triterpene α-onocerin, the little known ononid, and an essential oil whose concentration exhibits marked variation, which is also probably the reason for the drug's nonuniform effectiveness. Because collecting it in the wild is so laborious the spineless species *Ononis arvensis* is now being introduced into cultivation in the hope that this species will improve and stabilize the quality of the drug which has diuretic properties. It is used in the form of an infusion, one teaspoon of the finely crushed drug to one cup water to be taken three times daily. If the drug is not crushed then it is better to steep it for a lengthier period instead of briefly, the preparation and dosage remaining the same. Restharrow is advantageous in its diuretic action in that it does not irritate the kidneys and therefore is recommended for inflammation of the urinary tract and bladder as well as after colic caused by stones or gravel. It also proves beneficial in many instances of swollen ankles caused by high blood pressure, as well as giving relief in rheumatism. The drug is not often used by itself. Along with parsley root, licorice rhizomes and juniper berries it is an important component of diuretic herbal tea mixtures. Its medicinal effects have been known for thousands of years.

3

Spiny Restharrow (1) is a deeply-rooting subshrub generally less than half a metre in height. It has a scattered distribution on dry banks, rough grasslands, and at the edges of forests in warmer regions at lower elevations, chiefly on limestone substrates. The branched tap root grows from a multi-headed rhizome that becomes woody (2). It is one to two centimetres thick, crooked, twisted, often flattened on the inside. Whereas Spiny Restharrow is very prickly, the cultivated *Ononis arvensis* (3) is completely without spines or else with only a few spines which are soft and has leaves which are divided into three parts. The butterfly-like five-petalled flowers are arranged in loose, leafy hyacinth-like flowerheads which are present from June until September. The

corolla is purple, deep pink or whitish
with the standard glandular arrangement
on the outside, wings extending to its
halfway mark, and beaked keel. The
fruit is a hairy pod with one ripening
seed which is globe-shaped and
coloured brown with black spots.

1

2

Pot or **Wild Marjoram, Oregano**
Origanum vulgare L.

The genus *Origanum* is represented in the area from the Mediterranean region to India by about thirty species. Oregano is one of the hardiest of these. It is distributed throughout the temperate regions of Eurasia, its range extending to the Himalayas and central Siberia, elsewhere having been introduced. The flowering stems are collected in high summer, in dry weather. The constituents are made up of an essential oil, varying greatly in composition depending on the plant's geographical source, as well as bitter principles, tannins and ancillary substances which have antiseptic, anti-inflammatory and expectorant properties and also aid digestion. One teaspoon of the crumbled drug infused in one cup water is taken two to three times daily. Oregano also makes a refreshing and invigorating bath additive in a dilution of two tablespoons of the drug to two litres of water to treat rheumatic pains and skin infections, and as a gargle in gum disease and upper respiratory tract infections. As well, inhalation of the vapours has a beneficial effect on coughs and colds. Two other species of the *Labiatae* family are used for the same purposes as Oregano. They are Yssop (*Hyssopus officinalis* — 3), and Savory (*Satureja hortensis* — 4), both native to the region extending from the Mediterranean to Iran. Each species contains essential oil and tannins, and the dosage as well as uses are similar. All three of the above mentioned herbs were used medicinally in the Greek, Roman and Arab civilizations. They are also excellent culinary herbs both in terms of the aroma and flavour they give to foods and their usefulness in aiding digestion.

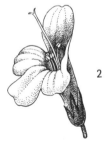

Oregano (1) is a warmth-loving perennial herb which grows on sunny banks, dry meadows and clearings from lowland to mountain elevations. It has a woody rhizome and reddish, hairy, four-angled stem just over half a metre in height. The leaves are opposite, short-stalked and ovate, larger at the bottom of the stem than towards the top. All parts of the plant are pleasantly aromatic. The flowers (2), which occur from July until September, in terminal arrangements, have a bell-shaped, five-toothed calyx and two-lipped corolla coloured carmine to red from which the stamens protrude; the upper

lip is straight and shallowly notched, the
lower lip three-lobed and downcurved.
There is a glandular, nectar-producing
ring at the base of the ovary, and the
fruit consists of brown, longish-ovoid
nutlets.

149

Parsley
Petroselinum crispum (MILL.) A. V. HILL   Umbelliferae

The genus *Petroselinum* originated in the Mediterranean region. It is comprised of four cultivated species. Of these, Parsley is the most widely grown, primarily as a culinary herb, however the fruits and roots are collected for medicinal purposes—the roots in the autumn of the first year, the fruits in the second year. The main constituent is a diuretic essential oil—a much greater amount occurring in the fruits than in the roots (2.6 percent compared with 0.1 to 0.3 percent). It follows therefore that the drug from the fruits is more potent than the drug from the roots. It should be administered in the form of an infusion made from a half teaspoonful of crushed fruits or two teaspoons of the crushed root to one cup water taken several times a day. The drug from the root should be included in treatment and not viewed as negligible for besides essential oil it also contains flavonoid components which assist the diuretic and antiseptic action of the drug. Parsley is recommended for inflammation of the bladder and urinary tract and following inflammation of the prostate gland. Parsley derivatives are usually found in diuretic herbal tea mixtures, however substituting Wild Parsnip (*Pastinaca sativa*) for its similar properties is inadmissable because its constituents have undesirable side effects.

Parsley (1) is a hairless biennial herb with a fleshy, spindle-shaped root up to twenty centimetres long (2). In the first year it produces a rosette of basal leaves, in the second year flowering stems up to one metre high. The leaves have cuts reaching nearly to the mid-rib; the basal leaves are in a loose rosette, the stem leaves thinly spaced and encased by a sheath where they join the stem. The umbrella-shaped flowerhead is comprised of between eight and twenty smaller umbrellas, or 'umbellets'. The flowers have an indistinct calyx and yellowish or reddish petals. The fruit is a very small, around two millimetres in length, ovoid, double achene, broader at the base and with a glandular disc on top, that splits into two low-ribbed achenes as seen in the schematic cross-section (3). The ribs contain conductive tissue and located between the ribs are ducts containing essential oil. All parts of the plant are pleasantly aromatic.

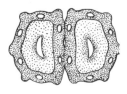

3

WARNING: Lengthy treatment with
very strong doses of Parsley is advised
against because this may cause severe
inflammation of the nerves. Nor should
it be taken during pregnancy because of
the danger of miscarriage.

1

2

151

Anise, Aniseed
Pimpinella anisum L.

Umbelliferae

The genus *Pimpinella,* numbering some one hundred and fifty species, is native to Eurasia and Africa. Anise, cultivated since ancient times, is indigenous to the eastern Mediterranean. *Pimpinella cretica* from the Aegean region is believed to be its wild ancestor. Anise is grown commercially in Spain and Italy, in warm parts of the USSR and to a limited degree in central Europe. It is also widely grown in Central America and Japan. The fruits—double achenes—are used medicinally and as a flavouring agent. They contain up to 3 percent of an essential oil with anethole as its main component plus about 30 percent fatty oil, proteins and sugars which have an excellent expectorant action in diseases of the upper respiratory tract. The drug is administered as an infusion of one less-than-full teaspoon of crushed fruits to one cup water taken three times daily. The infusion, which may be sweetened with honey, has a pleasant taste and is suitable mainly for children. As well as its effectiveness in respiratory ailments, the drug is also helpful in the relief of painful flatulence. It is a good stomachic and also has a mild diuretic action. In the cosmetics industry it is an aromatic and antiseptic ingredient of toothpastes and mouthwashes. Externally it is used as an insect repellent and in the past was recommended for the treatment of scabies. Anise is widely used as a culinary herb, in the food industry, and to flavour liqueurs. It is one of the world's oldest medicinal herbs.

Anise (1) is a slender, very aromatic, annual herb. The spindle-shaped root (2) bears a rounded, shallowly grooved stem branching at the top and reaching a height of half a metre. The lower leaves are stalked and round to kidney-shaped, the upper stem leaves have divisions reaching nearly to the mid-rib. The flowering period is from July until August. The flowerhead is umbrella-shaped and composed of seven to fifteen small umbrellas. The small flowers have loose involucres, an indistinct calyx and white corolla. The fruit is an ovoid to elongate double achene narrowing at the top. Only with difficulty do they separate into two achenes with five or more ledge-like ribs. The schematic cross-section of the fruit (3) shows that the ribs contain bundles of conductive tissue and that there are numerous ducts carrying essential oil round the entire periphery. Often used instead of aniseed oil is the essential oil from the star-shaped fruits of Star Anise (*Ilicium verum*), an evergreen tree native to east Asia.

152

1

2

3

153

Burnet Saxifrage
Pimpinella saxifraga L.

Umbelliferae

Burnet Saxifrage is native to practically all of Europe and western Asia, its range extending from Pakistan to central Siberia. It is also distributed in North America and New Zealand, where it was introduced. It is an extremely variable species. Also gathered for pharmaceutical purposes is the closely related Greater Burnet Saxifrage (*Pimpinella major*), the roots of both being collected in the wild in the autumn. The drug has a strong, distinct odour and pungent flavour, and contains an essential oil (0.4 percent), saponins, coumarin derivatives, tannins and ancillary substances. In the Middle Ages it was believed to ward off the plague. Nowadays it is used for its good expectorant properties in treating diseases of the upper respiratory tract, pharyngitis, bronchitis, and tracheitis, particularly when all other treatment has failed, and is also found to be of some use in the treatment of asthma. It is administered in the form of an infusion—one teaspoon of the crushed drug to one cup water, to be taken twice daily; it is also recommended to gargle with the infusion several times a day. The tincture from the drug may also be used, in a dosage of twenty drops three to four times daily in a cup of tea. Externally Burnet Saxifrage is a well-known popular remedy for treating slow healing wounds by bathing with an infusion prepared from two tablespoons of the drug to one litre of water. It is occasionally recommended as a remedy for inflammation of the urinary tract and to prevent the formation of kidney stones and gravel. Young leaves of the plant are eaten as a salad or used to flavour sauces.

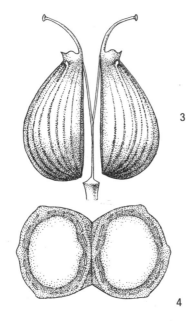

3

4

Burnet Saxifrage (1) is a perennial herb, generally grey and downy, with a spindle-shaped tap root (2) that contains a 'milk' smelling strongly of resin. It grows in dry meadows and pastures, on rocky banks, and in open woods from lowland to mountain elevations. The stem, rising from a basal rosette of odd-pinnate leaves, reaches a height of half a metre and the flowers, which are present from June until October, take the form of an umbrella-shaped cluster composed of between six and twenty umbellets. The flowers are radiate and five-petalled. The calyx is indistinct, the corolla white to purple and bristly on the outside. The fruit is a small, ovoid-globose double achene about two millimetres long (3)

154

that splits from the base when ripe into two achenes with five main, practically imperceptible low ribs and minute auxiliary ribs. This is clearly evident in the schematic cross-section (4).

155

Ribwort Plantain
Plantago lanceolata L.

Plantaginaceae

The genus *Plantago* with its approximately two hundred and sixty species is distributed in the temperate regions of both hemispheres. Ribwort Plantain, which is extremely variable in shape, is native to Europe, western Asia to the Himalayas and Tien Shan, and also north Africa. Nowadays, however, it grows in abundance even outside these regions. The leaves are used medicinally; they contain a large amount of mucilage, the glycoside aucubin, substances with an antibiotic effect, plus tannins and silicic acid. They must be gathered and dried with care because if crushed they turn brown and lose their potency. Ribwort is also cultivated on larger tracts where it is necessary to keep a careful check on the drug's quality, more so than when the leaves are gathered in the wild. Ribwort is one of the most popular medicinal herbs for home remedies. It is commonly used to treat inflammation of the upper respiratory passages, coughs, and for digestive disorders and externally for slow-healing wounds. It is used in the form of an infusion (steeped briefly or for several hours)—one teaspoon of the crumbled drug to one cup water, taken three to five times daily. This may be sweetened with honey. Ribwort syrup or juice pressed from the fresh leaves, thickened and sweetened with honey, may be used for the same purpose. The dosage is similar (one teaspoon, three to five times daily). Preparations from Ribwort are recommended chiefly for children to treat diseases associated with chilling. For external application to wounds it is recommended to use the pressed juice from well-washed fresh leaves, or to bathe them with the infusion from the drug steeped for several hours. Applying freshly ground leaves to swellings, bruises and superficial wounds also has a beneficial effect.

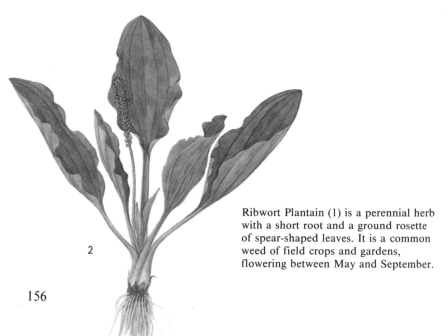

2

Ribwort Plantain (1) is a perennial herb with a short root and a ground rosette of spear-shaped leaves. It is a common weed of field crops and gardens, flowering between May and September.

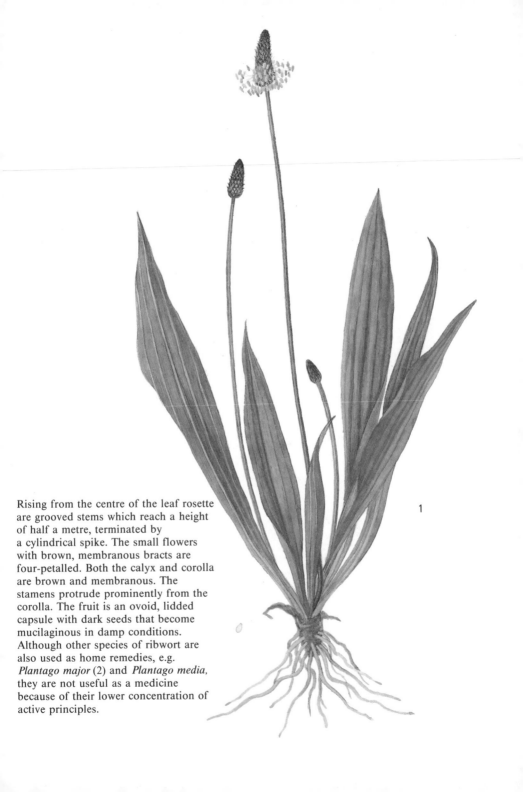

Rising from the centre of the leaf rosette
are grooved stems which reach a height
of half a metre, terminated by
a cylindrical spike. The small flowers
with brown, membranous bracts are
four-petalled. Both the calyx and corolla
are brown and membranous. The
stamens protrude prominently from the
corolla. The fruit is an ovoid, lidded
capsule with dark seeds that become
mucilaginous in damp conditions.
Although other species of ribwort are
also used as home remedies, e.g.
Plantago major (2) and *Plantago media,*
they are not useful as a medicine
because of their lower concentration of
active principles.

1

Waterpepper, Smartweed
Polygonum hydropiper L.

Polygonaceae

It is from the genus *Polygonum,* numbering some two hundred species with a worldwide distribution, that the family Polygonaceae takes its name. Waterpepper is found in Eurasia and is one of the oldest medicinal herbs used by man. The flowering stems contain an essential oil in the leaf and stem glands with the sesquiterpene izotadeonal, which has a burning peppery taste. They also contain substances close to fagopyrin (mentioned previously in connection with Buckwheat), for example, rutin, plus tannins and other constituents. The drug has astringent properties which prove useful in the treatment of haemorrhoidal and chronic menstrual bleeding. It is purported to have a diuretic action, but this is doubtful. The drug is used in the form of an infusion prepared from one tablespoon of the drug to one cup water, taken in the morning and evening. Sometimes used for the same purpose is the root of the related Common Bistort (*Polygonum bistorta*). The flowering stems of Knotgrass (*Polygonum aviculare*) contain partly soluble silicic acid, tannins and flavonoid glycosides which are also used medicinally. This also has an astringent action to some degree but because of the silicic acid in its tissues it is used more for diseases of the respiratory tract, e.g. pharyngitis, bronchial cough, asthma, and formerly also tuberculosis. It is administered in the form of an infusion prepared from one teaspoon of the ground drug to one cup water or a briefly boiled decoction, taken two to three times daily.

2

Waterpepper (1) is an annual herb, reaching a height of a half metre, distributed in damp and wet places and in shallow water alongside ponds, in ditches, etc., in lowland as well as submontane elevations. The stem is jointed with swollen nodes, by means of which it may also take root. The leaves are spear-shaped with translucent dots, which are glands filled with essential oil, submerged in the tissue of the leaf blade. Small, nondescript, yellow-green to pinkish flowers, arranged in loose spikes, are present from June until October. The fruits are small achenes enclosed in the persistent perianth. Pale Persicaria (*Polygonum lapathifolium* — 2) is another species belonging to this genus and found in like habitats.

1

However it is a larger plant, reaching
a height of one metre. The stems are
used medicinally for diseases of the
urinary tract and purportedly dissolves
kidney stones. The dosage is the same as
for Knotgrass.

Silverweed
Potentilla anserina L.

The genus *Potentilla* numbers some three hundred described species, which are chiefly distributed in the temperate regions of the northern hemisphere. Two of these are familiar medicinal herbs: Silverweed, which today has a worldwide distribution, and Tormentil (*Potentilla erecta*), native to Europe, western Siberia and the Middle East. The composition of the active principles is more or less the same in both species, therefore both have the same uses. In the case of Silverweed it is the dried flowering stems that are used medicinally, in the case of Tormentil it is the dried rootstock. The drugs contain chiefly flavonoid compounds and catechol tannins as well as constipating, anti-flammatory and anti-spasmodic properties, which also determine their use in the treatment of chronic nonspecific diarrhoeas. They are used primarily for those who do not tolerate sulfa drugs. Their occasional recommended use to relieve menstrual pains is, however, ineffective. The dried flowering stems are prepared in the form of a briefly steeped infusion—one teaspoon of the crumbled drug to one cup boiling water. The drug from the root is steeped in tepid water for four to six hours (one teaspoon of the crushed drug to one cup water); then the liquid is poured off and 1 cup of boiling water is poured over the drug. The first infusion and the liquids from the steeped root are combined and the resulting brew is taken in small drafts by the spoonful during the course of the day. The alcohol extract from the roots of both species (twenty to thirty drops in a glass of water) is used externally with success for gargling or for swabbing inflamed gums.

3

Silverweed (1) is a low, perennial herb with prostrate rooting branches, the stem rising from a thick rhizome. It grows in damp places, on waste ground, roadsides and around rural dwellings from lowland to submontane elevations.

The odd-pinnate leaves with interjected leaflets are generally smooth on the upper surface and silky white-felted below. The flowers (2), which are present from May until August, are relatively large, up to two centimetres in diameter, with five golden-yellow petals which are longer than the sepals. The fruit is a grooved achene. Unlike Silverweed, Tormentil (3) is a medium-sized perennial herb with erect stems and smaller yellow, long-stalked, four-petalled flowers which are present from May until September. It grows abundantly in meadows, heaths and open woods. In central Europe it is perhaps the commonest species of *Potentilla*.

2

1

Oxlip
Primula elatior (L.) Hill

Primulaceae

The genus *Primula* is a very large one comprising five hundred species. The centres of origin of the largest number of species are the eastern Himalayas and Yunnan in southwest China. From here come the greatest discoveries of this genus, so important as garden ornamentals. Used medicinally in Europe is the Oxlip, an extremely variable species indigenous to Europe and western Asia. The Cowslip (*Primula veris*) has a similar distribution and medicinal uses. The part used for the extraction of the active principles is the rootstock. Only when this is in short supply, due to the necessary protection of the plant and prohibited collecting of the roots in many countries, are the flowers gathered for this purpose as well. The drug contains chiefly saponins (the rootstock five times more than the flowers), and an essential oil of thick consistency. Other glycosidic substances are also present in the drug obtained from the flowers. The drug's expectorant action stems mainly from the saponins present, which ease the expulsion of phlegm from the upper respiratory tract in chronic bronchitis. The daily dosage is two to three cups of the infusion or decoction, prepared from one teaspoon of the crushed root per one cup water, to be taken in small drafts. The crumbled drug from the flowers is prepared in the form of an infusion from one tablespoon of the drug per one cup water and taken in the same way. The drugs are present in many pharmaceutical preparations designed to ease coughing, generally in the form of an extract. In view of the therapeutic importance of the drug obtained from the rootstock commercial cultivation of Oxlip is being considered.

Oxlip (1) is a perennial herb reaching a height of thirty centimetres with short rhizome from which grows a basal rosette of leaves and a long leafless stem. It is found in hilly country and at higher elevations, but does not occur in warmer regions and lowland districts. The leaves are at first curved underneath on the margin; they are wrinkled, longish-ovate, irregularly edged with rounded teeth and coloured green on the upper surface and grey-green below. The stem rising from the centre of the leaf rosette is terminated by a one-sided umbrella-shaped floral arrangement later than that of Cowslip. The calyx is pressed tightly to the corolla tube and is divided into long pointed teeth. The corolla is coloured sulphur-yellow and has a flat limb. The capsule containing the seeds is twice as long as the calyx.

162

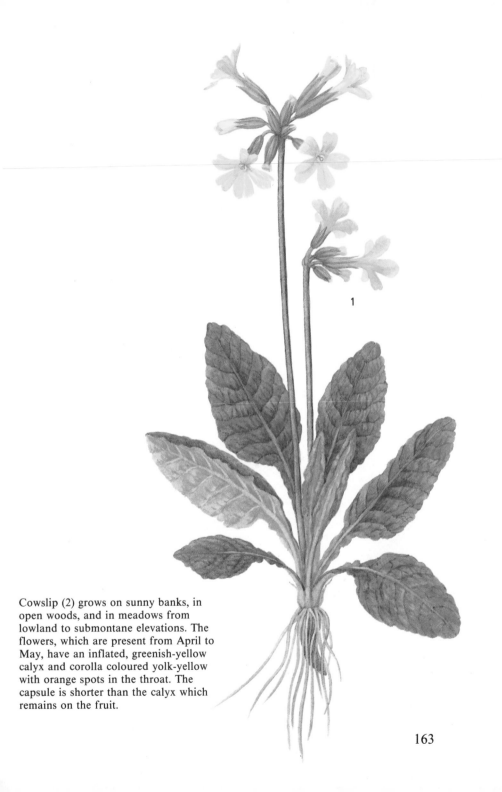

1

Cowslip (2) grows on sunny banks, in open woods, and in meadows from lowland to submontane elevations. The flowers, which are present from April to May, have an inflated, greenish-yellow calyx and corolla coloured yolk-yellow with orange spots in the throat. The capsule is shorter than the calyx which remains on the fruit.

163

Blackthorn, Sloe
Prunus spinosa L.

Rosaceae

The genus *Prunus,* comprising approximately two hundred species, has its centre of origin most probably in east Asia and is the source of a number of fruit trees and shrubs of economic importance such as apricot, cherry, almond, peach and plum. Compared with these, Blackthorn is of little importance, but the leafless shrubs covered with delicate white flowers are a sight to behold in early spring. They are not only pleasant to look at, but are useful medicinally; they contain chiefly flavonoid glycosides and have mildly diuretic and laxative properties. The infusion made from two teaspoons of the drug to one cup water is taken two to three times daily, and may be used as a mild laxative for both children and old people. It is also good for preventing diseases associated with chilling and for treating locomotor difficulties caused by rheumatism. The drug's advantages are its mild action and absolute harmlessness. The fruits are occasionally used in folk medicine in the form of home-made wine or liqueur to improve the body metabolism and prevent aging. It is not advisable to use the fruits by themselves because of their high concentration of tannins. The drug from the flowers may be obtained solely by gathering them in the wild. Because the shrub's thorniness prevents their rapid and effective collection the flowers are shaken onto sheets placed under the shrub and then, after all impurities such as twigs and leaves have been removed, spread out in thin layers and dried rapidly so as to preserve their original colour. The drug from the flowers is an ingredient of certain herbal tea mixtures to which it gives an attractive colour.

Blackthorn is a spreading, many-branched, spiny shrub reaching a height of three metres, which often forms dense thickets or spreading masses. It grows on shrubby hillsides, in forest margins and in woodland clearings from lowland to mountain elevations. The flowers (1) appear before the leaves (2), which are relatively small. They generally open from March to April, depending on the location and altitude, and often completely cover whole branches. The leaves are short-stalked, elliptic, and glandularly

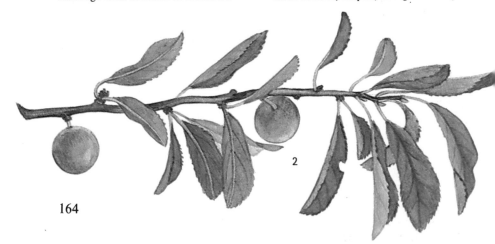

2

164

toothed on the margin. The white
flowers are sometimes solitary, more
often in clusters. They fall quite readily
and for that reason can be shaken off
the shrub. The fruits are small,
blue-black plum-like globe-shaped
stone-fruits with a whitish bloom and
astringent green flesh, measuring one to
one and a half centimetres across, some
of them remaining on the shrub
throughout the winter (3).

WARNING: The uncooked fruit of the
Blackthorn is poisonous.

165

Common Lungwort
Pulmonaria officinalis L.

Boraginaceae

The genus *Pulmonaria*, numbering some twelve species, is distributed throughout the temperate regions of Europe, from Great Britain to the Urals. Common Lungwort is one of the oldest of medicinal herbs. The scientific name is derived from the Latin word *pulmo*, meaning lungs, which the leaves greatly resemble by their shape, the likeness to diseased lungs being further underscored by the white spots on their surface. This species is an example of the medieval practice of treatment *per signaturam*, i. e. according to similarity between complaint and remedy. Nevertheless there are rational reasons for the use of the plant's leaves and flowering stems medicinally even today, for they contain partially soluble silicic acid, mucilage, saponins and other glycosidic substances with anti-inflammatory and healing properties. Nowadays it is used chiefly for treating diseases of the upper respiratory tract, namely chronic bronchitis, in the elderly. The drug also has a beneficial expectorant action, which is particularly welcome in elderly patients. It is used in the form of an infusion, one tablespoon of the crumbled drug to one cup water, to be taken three times daily after meals. Externally a similarly prepared infusion is used in greater quantity for bathing bleeding haemorrhoids. Lungwort is an ingredient of numerous herbal teas used for treating chest complaints. The current demand for the drug is relatively small and for the time being collection in the wild is sufficient. The leaves and stems must be spread out and dried rapidly, as if they are dried slowly and layered they readily turn brown and become less potent. When dried excessively the drug is crumbly. A word of warning — Lungwort easily becomes mouldy.

Common Lungwort (1) is a perennial herb of meadowland, damp woods and humusy soils in lowland as well as foothill districts. The branched rhizome bears leafy as well as flowering stems coloured a fresh green and roughly bristly. During the flowering period, from March until May, they reach a height of about thirty centimetres. The leaves are short-stalked or with no stalk at all. The short-stalked flowers are five-petalled, with bell-shaped calyx and funnel-shaped corolla, coloured purplish at first but later turning bluish. The fruit consists of four egg-shaped, faintly keeled, glossy, dark nutlets. The species is extremely variable and is generally divided by present-day botanists into two separate species: *Pulmonaria officinalis* L. and *Pulmonaria obscura* Dumort. The first species has spotted leaves arranged in a rosette which remains throughout the winter, the leaves of the second are without spots and the leaf rosette lasts only throughout the summer.

166

1

Common Oak, English or Pedunculate Oak
Quercus robur L. Fabaceae

The northern hemisphere is the home of several hundred species belonging to the ancient genus *Quercus*. The size of these trees and their hard, tough wood have made them revered since time immemorial and it is not surprising that the oak became the symbol not only of the Greek god Zeus but of the Old Germanic god Donar as well. Oaks have an immense variety of uses. The smooth, mirror bark from thicker branches or young boles is used for pharmaceutical purposes. It is generally obtained during the thinning of forests in young oak stands. The drug usually contains more than 10 percent catechol tannins and their ancillary substances and is used chiefly externally. The tannins have an astringent action and are very effective in the treatment of chilblains, frostbite, haemorrhoids, and itchy and festering rashes. Oak bark's advantage is that it does not irritate the skin or mucous membranes. Used for bathing or in compresses is a decoction made from five tablespoons of the crushed drug boiled in one litre of water for about twenty minutes. It should be prepared fresh every day. The crude drug should not be older than two years. Compresses should be changed several times; this should always be done before they begin to dry out, in other words about every twenty minutes. Always use porous material for compresses! Treatment, consisting of the application of three to five successive wet compresses, should be repeated two to three times daily, otherwise the results will not be very rewarding. Internally the drug is used for diarrhoea only in veterinary medicine.

2

Common Oak (1) is a deciduous tree with irregular crown and bark that is smooth at first, later deeply fissured. It attains enormous proportions. It is a component of oak woods, is planted out on levees, in flood-plain forests, as a solitary specimen dominating the landscape, and as a lovely ornamental in parks. The leaves are short-stalked, feather-shaped, with a lobed, wavy edge, and 'ears', auricles, at the base. The male flowers are in loose pendulous catkins and have a yellow-green

1

perianth. The female flowers are in
a cup-shaped container and have red
perianth segments. The fruit is
a smooth-skinned, stalked achene — the
acorn, the bottom third of which is
enclosed in the cup. The bark of the
closely related Sessile or Durmast Oak
(*Quercus petraea* — 2), may also be used
for pharmaceutical purposes. The leaves
of this oak are long-stalked and
wedge-shaped at the base and the acorns
(3) have no stalk.

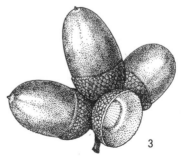

3

Alder Buckthorn
Rhamnus frangula L.   Rhamnaceae

Alder Buckthorn is native to the temperate regions of Eurasia. The bark peeled from young twigs (2) with no wood adhering to it is used. It must not be more than two millimetres thick and the layer of lichens must be scraped off. As it dries the cleaned bark curls into a cylinder, remaining yellowish-red on the inside. It is obtained in the wild, but for commercial purposes Alder Buckthorn may be cultivated on large tracts in forest establishments. Before it can be used the drug must either be stored for one year or heat-treated for approximately one hour at a temperature of up to 100 °C. This is necessary in order to change, either by natural or by artificial means, the glucofrangulin dianthrones in the fresh bark into anthracene derivatives that have a laxative effect because the former substances cause severe vomiting. Although this alteration may be achieved by either method, heat-treatment at a high temperature is preferable. The drug, or rather the decoction made from the drug, has a mild laxative action. It is recommended for chronic constipation and where it is desirable to avoid strong irritation of the intestines. The dosage is one teaspoon of the crushed drug per cup of the decoction taken at bedtime or else two to three cups during the course of the day. The decoction must not be taken by nursing mothers because the anthracene derivatives pass into the mother's milk. In European medicine the bark of Alder Buckthorn was formerly used for treatment in place of rhubarb, which was imported only for more well-to-do patients. Hence also its pharmaceutical designation at that time — *Rhabarbarum plebejorum.* However, it is by no means a less effective substitute.

Alder Buckthorn (1) is a robust shrub growing from one to five metres in height with slender, brittle, thornless branches and smooth, glossy, grey-brown bark exhibiting numerous pale spots (stomata). It grows on acidic soils in alder groves, damp woods and thickets from lowland to mountain elevations. The alternate leaves are short-stalked and prominently veined. The flowering period is from May till June. The small, greenish-white flowers, present from May until June, are arranged in loose clusters of between ten and twenty. The shrub bears a small globe-shaped stone-fruit with two or three seeds, coloured red at first and

2

later violet-black on ripening. The flowers appear in succession and so there may be buds, flowers, and unripe as well as ripening fruits on a single shrub all at the same time.

WARNING: Alder Buckthorn bark must be at least one year in storage before use: it should not be used in constipation due to tension, for long periods as a laxative, or by nursing mothers.

Black Currant
Ribes nigrum L.

Saxifragaceae

The one hundred and fifty species of the genus *Ribes* include among their number shrubs familiar for their fruit — gooseberries and currants. Black Currant is native to or else naturalized in Europe, Asia, the Caucasus, Himalayas, and Manchuria. The leaves are used medicinally and are generally gathered after the fruits. They must be clean and free of fungi and pests and as well as from the wild, may also be collected from shrubs cultivated on plantations for the fruit which is rich in vitamin C. The leaves contain flavonoids, catechol tannins, and traces of an essential oil. They also contain vitamins C and P and hitherto unspecified substances with bactericidal properties. The drug is used as a diuretic and to induce perspiration in the treatment of flu and diseases associated with chilling. It also has a beneficial effect on digestive disorders accompanied by diarrhoea and may be used as a tonic in convalescence. It is used in the form of an infusion — one teaspoon of the crumbled drug to one cup water — taken three to five cups daily. Natural juice from the fruit makes a refreshing, invigorating drink. It contains twice as much vitamin C as lemons or oranges. Today there is some evidence to suggest that vitamin C may help prevent flu and similar diseases. Although some people do not find the taste and smell of Black Currant particularly pleasant one can become accustomed to it or else the juice can be used in a mixture containing other, tastier juices.

2

Black Currant (1) is a spreading shrub more than one metre high mostly found nowadays in cultivation. The aroma of the leaves and fruits does not appeal to everyone. The leaves are stalked, alternate, palm-shaped with five lobes and numerous resinous glands on the underside. The bell-shaped, yellow-green to reddish, five-petalled flowers, which

172

1

are surrounded by a whorl of bracts, grow in loose multiflowered hyacinth-like clusters and are present from April until May. The fruit is a globe-shaped, long-stalked, black, glandular-spotted berry with numerous seeds. The seeds contain gamma-linolene acid in their fatty component which could be of great importance in geriatric medicine. In recent years the black fruits of the North American species *Aronia melanocarpa* (2), which likewise contain an important group of vitamins, chiefly vitamin C, have become popular as a source of vitamins.

Dog Rose
Rosa canina L.

Rosaceae

The genus *Rosa*, numbering some two hundred species and countless cultivated varieties, is found only in the northern hemisphere. The Dog Rose is
the commonest of the wild roses, mainly in Europe where it is widely distributed in the temperate regions, in the south only in the mountains, and also,
but less abundantly, in western Asia and northwest Africa. It is an extremely
variable species forming a group of approximately thirteen small species and
numerous hybrids. The ripe, deep red, undamaged hips (*Fructus cynosbati* in
pharmaceutical language), are the parts used medicinally. They are rich in vitamins, mainly vitamin C, vitamin A, B_1, B_2, and P, and also include carotenoids, tannins, sugars and organic acids. The drug has a mild diuretic, and
despite the presence of tannins, also a mild laxative effect. It is used as
a form of prevention against flu and diseases associated with chilling. For
convalescents, tea from the hips is invaluable for the tonic effect of the vitamins and for the dietetic properties of the drug which regenerate important
physiological functions. The tea is made by boiling or steeping one teaspoon
of the crushed hips per one cup water, which is then poured through a sieve
in order to remove the irritating hairs on the fruits. The dosage is four to six
cups per day. In diseases of the urinary tract it is recommended to drink two
to three litres of the tea daily; doing so for several days in succession has very
effective results. Cold rosehip tea is recommended as a refreshing drink for
persons with a fever. The fresh hips are made into purée, jelly, jam, and wine,
all rich in vitamins.

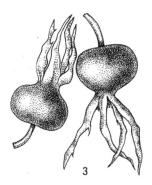

Dog Rose (1) is a shrub with arched,
downward-curving branches which are
armed with numerous stout hooked
prickles. In congenial conditions it may
even reach a height of three metres. It
grows in scrub, on field boundaries and
in hollows from lowland to submontane
elevations. Flower-bearing shoots are
without prickles. The leaves are alternate
and odd-pinnate with three and seven
pairs of leaflets. The flowers, which
appear from May till July, have five
wide-spreading petals and numerous
stamens. The fruit consists of hairy
achenes enclosed in the fleshy hip
topped by the remains of the calyx (2).
It was discovered that some species have
larger hips with more flesh and greater
concentration of vitamins, e. g. *Rosa
villosa*, the Ramanas Rose (*Rosa rugosa*)
(3), and others which are cultivated on
large tracts, on a large scale.

175

Rosemary
Rosmarinus officinalis L.   Labiatae

Rosemary is the only species in this genus. It is native to the Mediterranean region both on the European and African continent where it is a natural component of the evergreen brushwood known as the maquis. It is widely cultivated for its essential oil distilled for use in perfumery, less so for pharmaceutical purposes. The parts used medicinally are the leaves, which curl into a cylinder as they dry. In shape and colour they are more like needle-leaves. They contain one to two percent camphor-type essential oil, tannins and flavonoids. The quality and composition of the essential oil depend on the location and the time when the leaves are gathered. Administered internally, in small doses, the drug stimulates the digestion and also has a diuretic action. Rosemary is also used as a culinary herb for its effect on the digestion and the appetite. However larger doses have an undesirable irritant effect on the digestive tract as well as an intoxicating effect, for the drug stimulates the circulatory as well as nervous system. Its mildly inflammatory and antiseptic effect when used externally as a bath preparation is invaluable in the treatment of slow-healing wounds and rheumatic pains. It is used in the form of an infusion (one teaspoon of the crumbled drug to one cup boiling water taken two to three times daily between the main meals or after breakfast) as well as in the form of a bath preparation (one litre of boiling water is poured over four tablespoons of the drug and when it has been sufficiently steeped the liquid is poured into a warm bath). F. R. Weiss recommends bathing in the morning followed by a brief rest in bed, because bathing in the evening may cause insomnia.

2

Rosemary (1) is a small evergreen shrub with many-branched stems reaching a height of one and a half metres. The leaves are small, short-stalked and linear with a rolled-back margin. They have a pleasant fragrance when rubbed between the fingers. The flowers (2), growing in clusters of five to ten from the upper leaf axils, are five-petalled with bell-shaped, two-lipped calyx and corolla that is also two-lipped, twice as long as the calyx, and coloured blue-violet, very occasionally pink or white. The upper lip is deeply notched, the lower lip has a spoon-shaped middle lobe. The fruit consists of four nutlets. The first attempt to obtain the essential oil from the plant was round 100 A. D. by the physician Archigenes of Syria.

Rosemary oil is an important ingredient of cologne and other perfumery products.
NOTE: Because of possible side effects, Rosemary is a drug which should be used only when prescribed by a physician.

1

Madder, Dyer's Madder
Rubia tinctorum L.
Rubiaceae

The genus *Rubia,* with its forty species, can be found in the Mediterranean region as well as in Asia, Africa, Central America and South America. Most of the species have been a source of a natural red dye since ancient times and this holds true for Dyer's Madder as well. Native to the eastern Mediterranean region and Asia Minor, it was formerly widely cultivated in Europe for its colouring matter, alizarin, but this ceased in 1868 when alizarin began to be made synthetically from coal tar. The part used medicinally is the root which contains dark red anthracene derivatives (2 to 4 percent), chiefly alizarin, purpurin, rubiadin and others. Ruberythric acid is considered to be the main active principle. The drug's active principles are said to disintegrate or perhaps even dissolve calcareous magnesium, phosphatic and uratic stones in the kidneys and urinary bladder. This is now considered doubtful, the effects being explained as being the result of the abatement of spasms in the urinary tract due to the action of the entire group of active principles, thereby facilitating the elimination of the stones or gravel from the urinary tract. There is also some doubt as to the diuretic properties of these constituents, which are eliminated in the urine and give it a reddish tinge. The patient should be made aware of this fact so he will not think the red colour is caused by blood. The drug is administered in the form of a decoction (one teaspoon of the crushed drug to one cup water, boiled for about twenty minutes) taken three times daily after meals. In powder form it is taken in doses of one gram each, likewise three times per day, along with a pinch of bicarbonate of soda (on the tip of a knife). The extract from the drug is a component of many commercial pharmaceuticals.

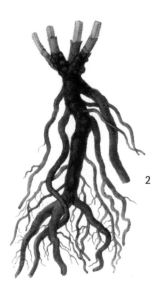

2

Dyer's Madder (1) is a perennial climbing herb with a relatively slender, jointed, much-branched, reddish rhizome and fibrous roots (2). Although cultivated it generally occurs as a naturalized plant. The stems are erect or climbing, between forty and a hundred centimetres long, and four-angled, with stiff, recurved spines on the edges that catch onto

neighbouring plants. The leaves, growing in whorls of four to six, are oval spears, prickly on the margins. The small flowers, arranged in loose terminal panicle-like inflorescences appear from June to August. They are four-petalled, stalked and coloured yellow. The plant produces a smooth, reddish-brown stone fruit about the size of a small pea.

1

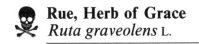

Rue, Herb of Grace
Ruta graveolens L.   Rutaceae

Rue is the most familiar and most widely used of the more than sixty species that make up this genus. It is probably indigenous to the Balkans and Crimea but has spread through cultivation (in central Europe from as far back as the 10th century) far beyond the borders of its native range. The leafy, flowering stems, which have completely superseded the once used leaves, are harvested by cutting two to three times a year. This must be done with care for contact with the sap from the cut stems causes a skin rash or oedemas in many people. The drug contains a toxic essential oil (0.7 percent), several alkaloids, furocoumarins and lignan derivatives. The medicinally important flavonol rutin was isolated for the first time from Rue, hence its name. ***The effect of strong doses of the large group of active principles is toxic and therefore increasing the dosage above the tested limit is dangerous.*** The drug has antispasmodic properties and is used to relieve gall bladder attacks and menstrual pains. Also well known is the drug's sedative action when it is administered in therapeutic doses to treat hot flushes during menopause, subjective complaints of nervous origin, and neurovegetative disorders. Dosage in the form of an infusion prepared from one teaspoon of the crumbled drug to one cup water taken in the morning after breakfast and in the evening an hour before bedtime is generally considered adequate. Rue is nowadays used medicinally only to a very limited degree. It is far more widely used as a flavouring agent. The top parts are also used for the recovery of the essential oil. Rue is sometimes grown as food for bees.

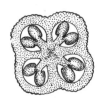

2

3

Rue (1) is a strongly aromatic perennial herb or subshrub with many-branched stem reaching a height of about seventy centimetres. The leaves, two to three times pinnately divided with spatula-shaped segments, are bluish-green and dotted with translucent essential oil ducts. The flowering period is from June until August; the flowers, arranged in dense terminal broad cone-shaped flower clusters in which the central flowers open first, are four-petalled apart from the uppermost flower which has five petals. The sepals are deciduous, the petals spatula-shaped, curved like a spoon, greenish-yellow and gland-dotted. The ovary is generally composed of four carpels (cross-section of ovary—2). The fruit is a four- to five-lobed capsule, or rather aggregate fruit of follicles with angular, warty seeds (3).

180

WARNING: Doses of this drug must be
kept low and never used in pregnancy
because of the risk of miscarriage.

1

181

Common or Garden Sage
Salvia officinalis L. Labiatae

The genus *Salvia,* comprising seven hundred species, is distributed mostly in the tropical and subtropical regions throughout the world. Most widely used medicinally is Common Sage, native to the Mediterranean region, where it occurs as three subspecies. The one most common on the drug market is subst. *minor,* which is indigenous to the area extending from Dalmatia to southeastern Serbia and Macedonia. The leaves or leafy stems without the lower woody parts are used. They are either collected in the wild or obtained from cultivated plants. Sage has been cultivated in Europe since the 9th century. The constituents include more than 2 percent of an essential oil, flavonoids, bitter principles and tannins. They have antiseptic and astringent properties and noteworthy is the fact that they lower the secretion of the sweat glands. The drug is administered both internally and externally. Internally it is recommended for treating inflammation of the upper respiratory passages and for digestive disorders in general. It curbs excessive sweating, e.g. during menopause, in neuroses, and in thyroid conditions. It is used in the form of an infusion (one teaspoon of the crumbled drug to one cup boiling water) taken two to three times daily between the main meals or at bedtime, or else in the form of an extract (twenty to thirty drops three times daily). Externally it is used primarily as an antiseptic mouthwash following dental surgery, as a gargle for sore throat (auxiliary treatment) and for bathing the skin in the treatment of various skin diseases, chiefly mycosis, a disease caused by parasitic fungi. The infusion for this purpose is prepared from one to two tablespoons of the drug to two cups water.

Common Sage (1) is a many-branched subshrub with woolly shoots reaching a height of eighty centimetres in its natural habitats, on sunny banks or around limestone rocks. The leaves are oblong, stiff, grey-felted and opposite each other, each pair being at right angles to the ones above and below it. The flowers are arranged in six to eight whorls of five to ten flowers each forming a spike-like cluster. The flowers which are present from May until July, are short-stalked, two-lipped, and coloured pale or dark violet (2). The upper lip is two-lobed, the lower lip three-lobed. The fruit consists of dark nutlets, and all parts of the plant have a pleasant fragrance. Other species of sage are also used medicinally, most often *Salvia sclarea,* which is likewise important in perfumery. The recently discovered Mexican species *Salvia divinorum* Epl. et Ját. which causes hallucinations, has attracted the attention of scientific circles.

2

WARNING: This drug should be
administered carefully and avoided
during pregnancy.

1

Elder
Sambucus nigra L.

Caprifoliaceae

The genus *Sambucus* numbers some thirty species distributed throughout the world. Elder has been a popular medicinal plant since ancient times. Formerly it was widely cultivated and because it readily spreads and becomes naturalized it is now considered a weedy shrub. Very occasionally it is cultivated on large tracts. It is believed to be indigenous to the waterside thickets and flood-plain forests of central Europe and western Asia. Both flowers and fruits are used medicinally. The flowers are collected from late spring until early summer by cutting off whole clusters from which the flowers are separated after they have dried. They contain flavonoids (rutin and quercetin), mucilage, tannins, and a small amount of a very aromatic essential oil. The fruits are gathered in the autumn before they are past their prime by cutting off the whole clusters and removing the stalks after they have dried. The fruits also contain the above-mentioned flavonoids, anthocyanin pigments, vitamins A, B, and C, and ancillary substances (sugars and organic acids). The flowers are very effective in producing perspiration and also possess mild diuretic, anti-inflammatory, antiseptic and mild laxative properties. An infusion used to treat colds and other infections associated with chilling can be prepared from one tablespoon of the drug to one cup water, taken five or more times daily. The infusion should be very warm and its effect may be enhanced by a hot foot bath. This mixture is also used as an ancillary medicine and gargle in the treatment of rhinitis-laryngitis, hoarseness, with chamomile for inflammation of the gums, etc. The fruits have similar properties. They are used mostly in the treatment of rheumatic pains, sciatica, neuralgias, including migraine, as well as stubborn coughs following incompletely cured diseases of the upper respiratory passages. In these cases, one teaspoon of the fruits briefly boiled in one cup water is taken three to five times daily.

Elder (1) is generally a large, spreading shrub, less often a tree, rarely more than six metres high. The leaves are opposite and odd-pinnate with oval, unequally serrate leaflets. The flowers, arranged in flat-topped terminal cymes, are regular, five-petalled, and have a tubular calyx and rotate, yellow-white corolla. The

2

tree produces small, black-violet, globe-shaped stone-fruits with three seeds and soft flesh that leaves a red-violet stain (2). The fruits are used as a source of natural red colouring matter, e.g. to add colour to beverages and foods. Also used in folk medicine to a limited degree are the related Red-berried Elder (*Sambucus racemosa*) and Dwarf Elder or Danewort (*Sambucus ebulus*). *These, however, are poisonous, and should not be used unless under the supervision of a qualified practitioner.*

Milk Thistle
Silybum marianum L. Gaertn.

Compositae

Milk Thistle has been cultivated in central Europe since the early Middle Ages as a medicinal plant taken over from ancient times. It was used primarily for digestive disorders of all kinds. The fruits—achenes—are the part used medicinally. They contain flavonolignans, i.e. a silymarin group of which silybin is the most effective, plus a large amount of fatty oil of excellent quality as a food. Tablets with specific proportions of the active constituents are used in medical practice for treating liver diseases such as hepatitis, cirrhosis, and poisoning caused by eating fungi containing toxic amantine or phalloidine which cause serious liver damage. Flavonolignans have a beneficial protective and detoxifying effect. Nowadays Milk Thistle is cultivated on a large scale in Europe as well as South America thus providing the pharmaceutical industry with sufficient amounts of the drug for the isolation of the silymarin group or of the individual pure flavonolignans. Nevertheless the drug itself is used in the treatment of gallstones accompanied by colic, chronic inflammation of the liver, and cirrhosis. It is taken in the form of an infusion prepared from one teaspoon of the crushed drug to one cup water, the dosage being three cups daily after meals or in the morning before breakfast and at bedtime. The tea should be relatively very warm and should be sipped slowly in small drafts. Recommended for persons who do not tolerate the tea is the water-alcohol extract *Tinctura Cardui Mariae* (twenty to thirty drops three to four times daily), which was already being recommended at the beginning of the 19th century by the well-known German physician J. H. Rademacher, contemporary of the renowned homeopath Hahnemann.

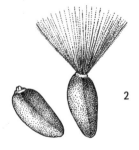

2

In central Europe Milk Thistle (1) is an annual herb, reaching a height of more than one metre, occasionally to be found as a temporarily naturalized escape. In its native land it is an overwintering annual or biennial. In the Mediterranean region this dangerously spiny plant is planted out as a hedge round fields to protect crops from grazing. In field cultivation it even reaches a height of more than two metres. The large, wavy-lobed, prickly, white-marbled basal leaves are arranged

186

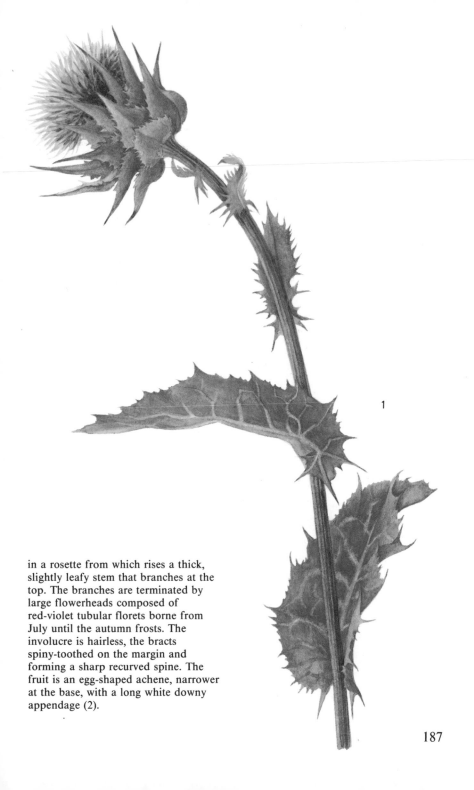

in a rosette from which rises a thick,
slightly leafy stem that branches at the
top. The branches are terminated by
large flowerheads composed of
red-violet tubular florets borne from
July until the autumn frosts. The
involucre is hairless, the bracts
spiny-toothed on the margin and
forming a sharp recurved spine. The
fruit is an egg-shaped achene, narrower
at the base, with a long white downy
appendage (2).

1

187

Common Comfrey
Symphytum officinale L.

Boraginaceae

Common Comfrey is a very old medicinal plant, one that was widely used particularly in the Middle Ages. It grows in Europe and western Siberia. More detailed investigation of the therapeutic properties of this ancient plant revealed that the constituents contained in the root, which is used medicinally even today, have excellent healing properties in the treatment of lesser as well as extensive bruises, thromboses, varicose ulcers, inflamed muscles as well as tendons, chronic diseases of the joints and bones, and stubborn wounds. The chief instruments of the drug's effect are the purin derivative allantoin, pyrrolizidine alkaloids and also ancillary substances such as tannins, organic acids and mucilage. The drug is used only externally in the form of liniments, ointments, compresses and bath preparations. Best suited for compresses are pressed gauze pads soaked in a decoction from the drug. The decoction is prepared from one tablespoon of the crushed drug to one cup water. Larger quantities, e.g. for bathing, may be prepared accordingly in the same proportion. Strict hygiene must be observed when applying the drug to infected wounds, varicose ulcers, haemorrhoids, in the treatment of inflammation of the bone marrow, etc. The drug must not be taken internally.

WARNING: The safety of this remedy is in question due to the presence of pyrrolizidine alkaloids, therefore excessive doses should be avoided.

3

Common Comfrey (1) is a tall herb, perceptibly roughly hairy to the touch, with a polycapitate, turnip-like root, sometimes called the 'blackroot', that is whitish inside and dark on the surface (2). It is gathered in spring before the flowering period or in the autumn after the flowers have faded. Comfrey grows in damp grassy places from lowland to submontane elevations, reaching a height of one metre. The stem is hollow, winged, and much-branched. The rather large, relatively thin leaves are oval spears in outline, wrinkled, and roughly hairy. The flowering period is from May until September. The flowers are arranged in nodding, broad, cone-shaped flower clusters in which the central flowers open first (3), growing from the upper leaf joints. They are five-petalled with long drooping stalks. The corolla is tubular-urn-shaped and generally coloured a dingy violet-purple. The stamens have violet anthers. The fruit consists of three-sided, smooth, dark nutlets.

188

189

Common Dandelion
Taraxacum officinale WIGGERS   Compositae

The genus *Taraxacum,* distributed throughout Eurasia, is extremely variable and only a few specialists are familiar with its internal systematics. This is due to its reproducing mostly by vegetative means and the transfer of characteristics from the parent organism coupled with occasional hybridization and repeated vegetative reproduction, or 'apomixis'. That is why hundreds of 'new small species' are being described nowadays. The composition of the active principles, however, does not vary much and so there is no need for any concern when collecting the plant for medicinal use. The roots or the roots together with the leaves are used. They contain bitter principles, tannins, glycosidic substances and inulin, and the milky sap constituents that have a beneficial effect on liver and kidney function. The leaves furthermore contain vitamins C and B2, pigments and other ancillary substances. The drug has a wide range of therapeutic uses. It has a beneficial effect on the function of the liver and kidneys in that it prevents the formation of gallstones and kidney stones, and if they are already present it aids in their elimination. That is why it is generally recommended for digestive and bowel disorders. It also relieves rheumatic complaints, including painful arthroses caused by the excessive formation of uric acid salts in cartilage and tendons. It is used in the form of an infusion prepared by briefly boiling one tablespoon of the crumbled drug per one cup water and then letting it steep for about twenty minutes. The dosage is one to two cups of the decoction taken in the morning and evening. Spring and autumn 'cures' consisting of drinking this brew for a period of one or two months can be very effective.

2

Dandelion (1) is a familiar plant with an overwintering, long, spindle-like root. All parts of the plant contain a milky sap that oozes profusely when the plant is cut or bruised. The leaves, arranged in a dense ground rosette, are extremely variable in shape and deeply pinnately divided. Dandelion is considered a very troublesome weed difficult to eradicate in excessively rich soils. Rising from the centre of the leaf rosette, mainly in

190

spring but also during the summer, are hollow scapes terminated by solitary heads of numerous yellow strap-shaped florets. The fruits, which form a fluffy ball when ripe, are spindle-shaped achenes (2) with an appendage of white hairs at the end of a long stem or 'beak' that enables the achenes to be dispersed even quite a distance from the parent plant.

Wild Thyme, Creeping Thyme
Thymus serpyllum L. emend. MILL.   Labiatae

This species is extremely variable both in terms of form as well as chemical characteristics, this being true of all members of the genus *Thymus*. It is an aggregate species comprising a great number of smaller species. Wild Thyme is distributed in the temperate regions of Eurasia, its range extending to the Himalayas and central China and there are isolated instances of its occurrence in Africa's Atlas Mountains and in Ethiopia. The densely leaved flowering stems, devoid of the lower, woody, leafless parts, are used medicinally. Their constituents include an essential oil (up to 1 percent) with thymol, bitter principles, tannins, and ancillary substances. It is useful for improving the digestion but it also has a beneficial effect on coughs and hoarseness. Put to good use in digestive disorders are its antispasmodic, sedative as well as antiseptic properties. It is used in the form of an infusion prepared from one tablespoon of the crumbled drug to one cup water taken three times daily. For diseases associated with chilling it is recommended to sweeten the infusion with honey or combine it with the drug from Ribwort. In folk medicine the drug has long been used as an admixture to baths for its refreshing, invigorating, as well as antiseptic effect, following a stint of hard work, on tired muscles and on exhaustion. For this purpose an infusion from 100 g of the drug is added to the bath water which should be sufficiently warm. The infusion is also recommended as an antiseptic mouthwash for inflammation of the gums and also as a gargle. An alcohol extract from the drug can also be used for this purpose. The pleasant fragrance, slightly bitter, spicy taste and good effects on the digestion are ample reason for using Wild Thyme in cooking and as a component of the herb base for aperitifs and liqueurs such as Chartreuse.

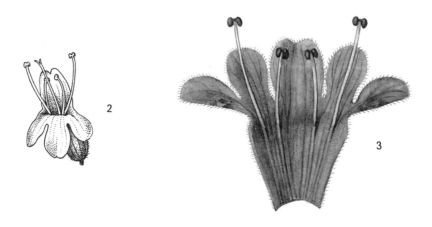

2

3

Wild Thyme (1) is a small, tufted perennial herb or subshrub with ascending stems that are woody at the base. It grows chiefly in warmer regions on sunny banks, in grasslands, on field boundaries, in sandy situations and in open woods from lowland to mountain elevations. It flowers from May till September. The stems grow to twenty centimetres high and vary widely both in type and hairiness. The minute leaves are opposite each other but each pair is at right angles to the ones above and below it and likewise extremely variable. The small flowers are arranged in pseudowhorls of three to eight in each forming terminal spike-like flower clusters. They are symmetrical (2, 3—longitudinal section of flower spread out flat), with bell-shaped calyx and two-lipped corolla coloured dark or pale violet-red. The group of stamens has two longer than the rest. The fruits are small, ellipsoid nutlets.

1

193

Garden or Common Thyme
Thymus vulgaris L.   Labiatae

Garden Thyme is native to the Iberian Peninsula, southern France, the western coast and south of Italy, and also Greece, where it grows on rocky slopes as one of the main components of the discontinuous tracts of hard-leaved plants, so-called *'tomillares'*. The flowering stems, gathered from wild or cultivated plants, contain chiefly an essential oil (often more than 3 percent) with thymol, carvacrol and cineol as the main components, as well as tannins, saponins, bitter principles and other glycosidic substances. Garden Thyme is used primarily for diseases of the upper respiratory passages. It dissolves mucus, relieves bronchial spasms, and has an antiseptic effect. It is an excellent expectorant with an antispasmodic action. It alleviates the difficulties of persons suffering from emphysema and asthma even though it is not a cure. It is used in the form of an infusion prepared from one teaspoon of the crumbled drug to one cup water taken three times daily. The drug is also effective in the treatment of digestive disorders and flatulence, where it exerts not only an antiseptic but also an antispasmodic action, for which reason Garden Thyme is a popular culinary herb. The dosage for digestive complaints is the same as for respiratory diseases; the drug may also be used in the form of an alcohol extract taken in drops. Garden Thyme may also be used as a dermatological agent for treating stubborn rashes, bathing chafed areas, fungus infections between the toes, etc., and as an addition to the invigorating and refreshing bath to relieve tired muscles and exhaustion. A 5 percent infusion is used for this purpose.

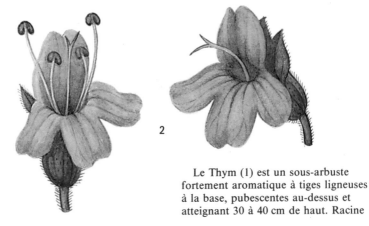

2

Le Thym (1) est un sous-arbuste fortement aromatique à tiges ligneuses à la base, pubescentes au-dessus et atteignant 30 à 40 cm de haut. Racine

194

Garden or Common Thyme (1) is
a strongly aromatic subshrub with stems
woody at the base, downy above, and
reaching a height of thirty to forty
centimetres. The root is long and
spindle-shaped. The small, decussate,
linear leaves have revolute margins, are
smooth-skinned above, white-felted
below, and glandularly spotted. The
spike-like clusters, present from May till

September, are composed of
pseudowhorls made up of three to six
flowers growing from the upper leaf
axils. The flowers (2) are small and
symmetrical with two stamens longer
than the others. The calyx is bell-shaped
and two-lipped. The corolla, likewise
two-lipped, is coloured white to pale
purple; the lower lip is three-lobed, the
upper lip flat and two-lobed. The fruits
are nutlets. The essential oil from
Garden Thyme is commonly used in
toothpastes, mouthwashes, etc.

1

195

Small-leaved Lime
Tilia cordata M<small>ILL.</small>

Tiliaceae

Most species of the family *Tiliaceae* are found in the tropics. The genus *Tilia* is somewhat of an exception, even though its range extends to the tropical regions of the northern hemisphere. Some twenty species of limes have been documented to date. Of these the Small-leaved Lime and Large-leaved Lime (*Tilia platyphyllos*) as well as hybrids of the two—*Tilia* × *vulgaris* Hayne—are used medicinally. The whole floral cluster, including the membranous bract, is collected. These are gathered in dry weather at the beginning of the flowering period. The drug must not be brown and must not contain flowers past their prime, or fruits. The flowers of the commonly cultivated Silver Lime (*Tilia tomentosa*) and American Lime (*Tilia americana*) cannot be used medicinally because the active principles are not present in adequate concentrations or proportion. The drug contains flavonoids, e.g. tilirosid, a small amount of an essential oil (max. 0.1 percent) with farnesol as the main component, mucilage, tannins and ancillary substances. It has anti-inflammatory, diuretic and mild antispasmodic properties as well as being useful in inducing perspiration, and is therefore widely used for diseases associated with chilling (with or without a temperature), namely respiratory catarrh, flu, cough and cold. One cup of boiling water is poured over one teaspoon of the crumbled drug and left to steep for ten to fifteen minutes in a covered vessel. The infusion should be drunk very warm and sweetened with honey; lemon juice may also be added. It should be taken in small drafts, the dosage being three to five cups daily. A herbal tea mixture of equal parts of lime, elderberry and chamomile flowers is very effective in inducing perspiration.

2

Limes (1) are large trees with a rather short trunk and large spherical crown. Solitary limes are an important feature of the landscape in the temperate regions of Eurasia. They are also widely cultivated. The leaves are asymmetrically veined, sharply serrate, dark green above and greyish green below, with rust-coloured hairs in the axils of the veins. The flowering period is from June till July. The flowers are arranged in clusters of between four and ten, and are apparent from June until July. They are stalked, radiate and five-petalled and have a characteristic honey-like fragrance. Joined to the stalk of the

196

flower-cluster is a large membranous bract with net-like markings. The sepals exude a nectar on the outer surface. The petals are long ovals coloured yellowish-white with stamens, which number between ten and thirty, arranged in five bundles. The fruit (2) is a soft, globe-shaped, short-pointed achene.

Fenugreek
Trigonella foenum-graecum L.

Leguminosae

Of the more than eighty species belonging to the genus *Trigonella* several have been widely cultivated as a fodder crop, Fenugreek being one such species. It is indigenous to Asia Minor, the Middle East, and Transcaucasia, but through cultivation has spread also to central Europe. The seeds, obtained exclusively from cultivated plants, have been used medicinally since the days of the Babylonian and Egyptian Empire. They contain mucilage, fatty oil, the alkaloid trigonelline, steroidal sapogenins, flavonoids and ancillary substances. The drug's use is determined mainly by the mucilage and its softening effect. It is used to treat swellings, inflammations with a discharge, boils, ulcers, and staphylococcus infections. The seeds are ground and mixed with water to make a warm doughy mass which is then applied to the affected area as a compress several times a day. The ground seeds may also be boiled with water to make a watery mush which may be used as an ointment. Which method is used is a matter of choice and depends on the patient's condition. Flax-seed may be used in more or less the same way, but the drug from the seeds of Fenugreek is more effective because of the alkaloid and sapogenin component. Affected areas may also be bathed with an infusion obtained by steeping the crushed drug in cold water (one part drug to ten parts water) for several hours. Fenugreek is used also in veterinary medicine, being added to feed in order to improve the appetite of domestic animals. As well as having culinary uses, the mucilages from the seeds are used to give a finish to certain fabrics in the textile industry. Fenugreek is an important honey plant.

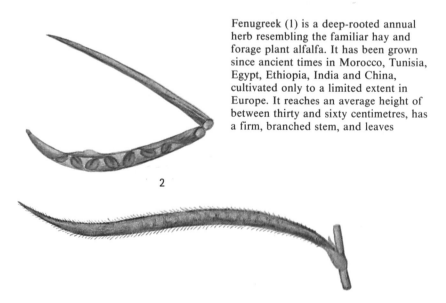

Fenugreek (1) is a deep-rooted annual herb resembling the familiar hay and forage plant alfalfa. It has been grown since ancient times in Morocco, Tunisia, Egypt, Ethiopia, India and China, cultivated only to a limited extent in Europe. It reaches an average height of between thirty and sixty centimetres, has a firm, branched stem, and leaves

2

comprised of three leaflets. In summer, pale yellow flowers grow singly or more often in pairs from the upper leaf axils. The fruit (2) is a slender, slightly curved pod up to ten centimetres long with an extended tip or 'beak' containing between ten and twenty pale brown seeds. The seeds are an important ingredient of special, pungent mixtures such as curry-powder and chutney, in India as well as in North and South America.

1

Nasturtium
Tropaeolum majus L.

Tropaeolaceae

Nasturtium was introduced to Europe from Peru in the late 17th century as a striking garden ornamental. The closely related *Tropaeolum minus* L. was already known in Europe as a garden ornamental shortly after the discovery of America. Its medicinal uses were only recognized in Europe when it was discovered that the benzylisothiocyanate resulting from fermentation of a constituent in the plant has important bactericidal properties. This was later than in its native South America. Its advantage is that it is relatively nontoxic and that pathogenic micro-organisms do not develop resistance to its effect as often happens in the case of antibiotics such as penicillin and streptomycin. The fruits, which are used medicinally, have one drawback in that they do not ripen all at the same time and readily fall from the plant, which is why this excellent drug is in short supply. Nasturtium can be used for treating stubborn infections of the urinary tract as well as for infections of the upper respiratory passages. An infusion is prepared by pouring one cup of boiling water over one teaspoon of the drug, crushed just before doing so, and allowing this to steep covered for twenty minutes. This is then taken in small drafts in a daily dose of three to five cups. The infusion should continue to be taken for several more days following the disappearance of symptoms in order to exclude the possibility of their recurrence. Commercially prepared pills and tablets used for treating urinary infections are coated with substances that prevent the release of the active principles until they have passed through the stomach and reached the small intestine. This greatly increases their effectiveness.

Nasturtium (1) is a perennial herb in its native South American home, in Europe it is grown as an annual. It has climbing stems which reach up to three metres in length and entire leaves that are

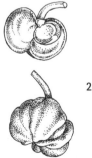

2

kidney-shaped to rounded with a stalk in the centre of the blade. The flowers, growing singly from the leaf axils, are stalked, from three to six centimetres across, symmetrical, and coloured yellow, orange or brownish-red. The calyx is prolonged into a prominent coloured spur from two to four centimetres long. The ovary has three chambers and when ripe divides from the centre outward into three, one-seeded fruits with thick, spongy, outer walls which later become corky and do not split open when ripe (2). The fruits of the ornamental coloured hybrids *Tropaeolum* × *cultorum* may also be used as a drug. The buds and young fruits may be preserved in vinegar and used as a substitute for capers, which are the buds of *Capparis spinosa* L.

1

Coltsfoot
Tussilago farfara L.

This, the only species of the genus *Tussilago,* is one of the most widespread weeds of Europe and Western Asia. Elsewhere it is an introduced plant that has become naturalized. The flowerheads, before they have passed their prime, along with the young leaves, are used in drug production. The flowers must be collected before they are fully open for otherwise they open during the drying process, ripen, and break up into downy achenes that are practically without any medicinal value. The drug from the flowers is sulphur-yellow with a honey-like aroma and mucilaginous bitter taste, the drug from the leaves is odourless and also has a mucilaginous, slightly bitter taste. Both drugs contain about 8 percent mucilage plus flavonoid glycosides, bitter principles, tannins and traces of pyrolizidine alkaloids. They have long been valued for their expectorant and antispasmodic properties in the treatment of inflammation of the upper respiratory passages accompanied by a cough. They also relieve coughing in patients with emphysema and silicosis. The drug from the leaves, or better yet the fresh leaves themselves are recommended in compresses for treating phlebitis, rheumatic pains, and boils. Primarily, however, Coltsfoot is used for treating diseases associated with chilling and accompanied by cough, particularly if the condition is chronic. The drug is used in the form of an infusion prepared from one tablespoon of the crumbled drug, either from the flowers or leaves, to one cup water, taken in the morning and evening, or an additional two to three cups, sweetened with honey, taken during the course of the day. The drugs from Coltsfoot are components of numerous herbal tea mixtures manufactured for the treatment of chest colds. Even though the drug is in great demand the supply from wild sources is sufficient.

Coltsfoot is a small perennial herb that spreads rapidly by means of the rhizomes with long runners. It grows abundantly in bare and waste ground, by roadsides, in ditches, rubbish dumps and in fields from lowland to mountain elevations. Early in spring scaly stems terminated by solitary golden-yellow flowerheads (1) grow from the flower buds. The round, veined leaves, which form a ground rosette (2), appear after flowering. They are long-stalked and up to thirty centimetres across. When they first appear the leaves are white-felted on both sides, later becoming smooth on the upper surface. A single flowerhead is composed of between two and three hundred flowers. The fruit is a long cylindrical achene with a long white appendage composed of several rings of hairs—the modified calyx of the individual flowers.

1

2

203

Stinging Nettle and Small Nettle
Urtica dioica L., *Urtica urens* L. Urticaceae

These two species of the genus *Urtica* are nowadays common weeds the world over, though they are native to Eurasia and Africa. Elsewhere, mainly in North and South America and Australia, they have become naturalized. The leaves and stems together with the leaves of both are used medicinally and contain practically the same constituents: a large amount of chlorophyll, vitamins A, B_2, C, E, and K_1, folic acid, histamine, acetylcholine, formic acid, acetic acid, and butyric acid, and fairly abundant mineral substances. These give nettle primarily diuretic, antirheumatic, and 'blood-purifying' properties, the latter being produced by the effect of speeding up the metabolism. Externally use is made of the inflammatory effect of the stinging hairs in the drug. The drug is used in the form of a decoction prepared from one teaspoon of crumbled leaves or one tablespoon of crumbled stems and leaves to one cup water, boiled briefly for five minutes, and taken three times daily, best of all after meals. It is used as a diuretic tea in the treatment of rheumatic complaints as well as for oedema caused by poor heart function and for circulatory disorders. According to R. F. Weiss it can be used as a reliable substitute for thiazide treatment without the latter's unpleasant side effects. In place of tea it is possible to use the pressed juice from freshly-picked plants which have first been ground. The dosage is one tablespoon three times daily taken for a period of four to six weeks. Externally, for rheumatic pains, lumbago, and sciatica, it is recommended to apply fresh nettles to the sore area two to three days in succession followed by an equally long interval before applying them again.

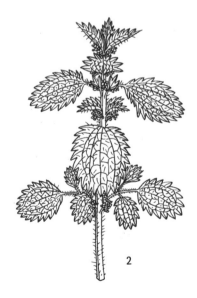

Stinging Nettle (1) is a robust perennial with a creeping rhizome that is difficult to eradicate and four-angled stems. All parts of the plant are covered with stinging hairs. The stalked leaves are heart-shaped at the base and coarsely serrate; the upper side is covered with appressed hairs and partly with long stinging hairs. The green flowers are arranged in long clusters of either male or female examples; the fruit is an ovoid achene. The species is quite variable. Small Nettle (2) is a much smaller annual herb reaching a height of only forty centimetres, in other words half the size of Stinging Nettle. Its sting, however, is sharper. The stems are soft, the leaves measuring two by three centimetres. The whole plant is covered only with stinging hairs. The flowers are unisexual, the plants self-pollinating, with more flowers in the female clusters than in the male clusters. Both flowers and achenes are coloured pale green.

1

Common Bilberry, Whortleberry, Blueberry
Vaccinium myrtillus L.

Ericaceae

The genus *Vaccinium* comprises a great many species — more than two hundred — most of them found in the northern hemisphere and in the mountains of tropical regions. Common Bilberry is found in the mountains of southern Europe, the Caucasus and Siberia. The leaves, which are used medicinally, contain approximately 10 percent catechol tannins, flavonoid glycosides, and glucokinins. The dried fruits are also used as a drug and contain, in addition to tannins, anthocyanin pigments, organic acids and vitamin C. They are very effective in the treatment of diarrhoea, dyspepsia and even dysentery and are recommended as an effective and innocuous remedy for small children. They are used in the form of a briefly boiled decoction made from one teaspoon of crushed dried fruits to one cup water, taken several times a day, best of all by the spoonful. Finely powdered dried fruits may also be briefly boiled in water. The resulting beverage in the form of a suspension is very effective in checking diarrhoea but must not be sweetened! Fresh berries with sugar and milk, on the other hand, have a mild laxative effect and are rich in vitamins. The drug from the leaves is a component of commercially prepared pharmaceuticals used in the treatment of diabetes. In folk medicine it is known for its antiseptic action on infections of the urinary tract. Here the action is not due to hydroquinone as in the closely related Cowberry but to flavonoid glycosides. It is used in the form of an infusion prepared from one teaspoon of the crushed leaves to one cup water to be taken three to four times daily in small drafts. The antiseptic and astringent effect of drugs both from the leaves and the berries is used in the form of a mouthwash-gargle for gum disease.

2

Common Bilberry (1) is a small, thickly-branched shrub with creeping rhizome and numerous erect, three-angled stems. It often forms spreading masses in pine woods, open coniferous forests and heaths. The leaves are short-stalked, oval, and deciduous. The flowers grow singly or in loose clusters in the upper leaf joints, from April until July. The rose-tinted corolla is a near spherical urn-shape with short teeth. The fruit is a globe-shaped, juicy, many-seeded berry. The closely related Cowberry or

1

Cranberry (2) (*Vaccinium vitis-idaea*) has
leaves that are very glossy on the upper
side and globe-shaped, glossy berries
coloured red when ripe. It is more
frost-resistant than Bilberry. The leaves,
which contain hydroquinone, have an
excellent antiseptic action on infections
of the urinary tract. The drug is used in
the form of an infusion prepared from
one teaspoon of finely crushed leaves to
one cup water steeped for several hours
or else as a briefly boiled decoction,
taken three times daily.

207

Common Valerian, All-heal
Valeriana officinalis L. s. l.

Valerianaceae

The genus *Valeriana* is very diverse, including, as it does, herbs and shrubs, as well as climbers. Common Valerian is indigenous to the whole of Eurasia and its root has been used medicinally since medieval days. It contains about 1 percent of an essential oil of widely differing composition, plus very effective but unstable valepotriates, isovaleric acid, and traces of pyridine alkaloids. Since collecting it in the wild is no longer sufficient to cover the great demand for the drug, the plant is now cultivated. Valerian is a reliable sedative and has a calming, anti-stress action. For this reason it is widely used in folk medicine for various neuroses, ranging from pathological agitation accompanied by headaches and insomnia to palpitations. It is most commonly used in the form of an infusion prepared by pouring one cup of boiling water over one teaspoon of the crushed root and letting it steep for twenty minutes. The resulting brew is then drunk slowly — two to three cups daily. An infusion prepared by pouring one glass of tepid water over one tablespoon of the crushed drug and letting it steep for about eight hours is recommended as a bedtime drink. The drug can also be used in the form of a tincture — one teaspoon on a lump of sugar or in water taken two to three times daily — as well as in the form of an extract. However, it is most widely used as a component in a great variety of commercial preparations and in suitable combinations with other drugs which enhance its effect. It may be possible to obtain the drug from closely related species which contain greater amounts of the active principles, and this is currently being investigated.

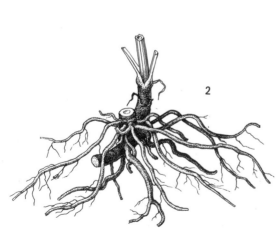

Common Valerian (1) is a perennial herb with shortly creeping, cylindrical rhizome and numerous wiry roots (2). The drug acquires its pronounced, distinctive odour only after drying. The plant grows randomly in meadows and on shrubby banks, usually alongside waterways. The stems are erect, hollow, and up to one metre high. The lower leaves (3) are stalked, the upper ones sessile and are extremely variable in shape. The flowers (4), arranged in loose, irregular flat-topped clusters, are small and asymmetrical; the corollas are pale pink to white and occur from May until September. The fruit is an achene with a long appendage formed from the feathery remains of the calyx teeth, a flying apparatus. The viability of the seeds is very limited, which is why its cultivation often meets with failure.

4

1

3

209

Common White Hellebore
Veratrum album L.

Liliaceae

The fewer than fifty species of the genus *Veratrum* are distributed in the northern hemisphere. Of these, White Hellebore is the one most familiar in Europe. Broadly, it is comprised of two species: *Veratrum album* L. and *Veratrum lobelianum*. The latter's range extends far to the east across Siberia to Manchuria and Japan. White Hellebore grows in the mountains of southern and Central Europe, mainly in the Alps. Green Hellebore (*Veratrum viride* Ait.) is found in North America. *All these species are of pharmaceutical importance but all are extremely toxic.* Used medicinally are the rhizomes and roots, which are pulled up in the autumn. They contain up to 1.5 percent of a rich group of alkaloids whose composition varies. The mutual proportion of the individual alkaloids or their absence is determined genetically as well as by the age of the plant and its location. Currently the drug is obtained exclusively by gathering the rootstock in the wild. In view of the relatively small demand and possibility of its import from the Balkans and the USSR Hellebore is not cultivated, even though in many places it has already become an endangered plant. Protoveratrine alkaloids lower blood pressure. They also have a pronounced antineuralgic action and have been used in the United States in the treatment of sudden and very intense neuralgic pains. Ointments containing the isolated alkaloids are also useful in the treatment of severe neuralgias. The drug is also prescribed in the form of a tincture.

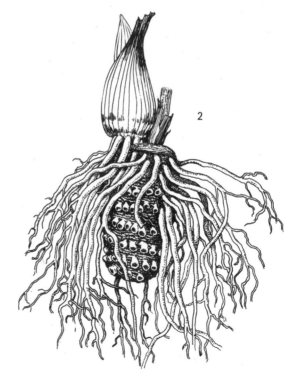

2

White Hellebore (1) is a perennial herb
of mountain meadows and sloping
ground beside springs. A characteristic
feature of the plant is the short, dark,
bulbous rhizome with mass of thin, wiry,
lighter-coloured roots growing from the
base (2). The robust stems, generally
more than one metre high, are thickly
covered with leaves. The large ovate to
spear-shaped leaves have sheathing
bases, are longitudinally grooved, and
downy on the underside. The flowering
period is from June till August. The
flowers, present from June until August
and arranged in long flower clusters up
to half a metre in length, are trimerous
and the perianth segments are
whitish-green, yellowish or white. The
fruit is a capsule splitting at maturity
into three follicles with numerous
winged seeds. The drug is odourless, but
provokes fits of sneezing. In former days
it was added to snuff.

WARNING: Preparations made from
this drug should never be used for self
medication; without the supervision of
a physician they may prove fatal. Its use
is restricted under the Medicines Act
1968.

1

211

Large-flowered Mullein
Verbascum densiflorum BERTOL.   Scrophulariaceae

Of the more than three hundred and fifty species of the genus *Verbascum* distributed throughout Eurasia mainly Large-flowered Mullein is of medicinal value. The parts collected for medicinal purposes are the petals and stamens which are pulled out of the calyx. They contain chiefly mucilages, plus saponins, carotenoid pigments, flavonoid glycosides and traces of an essential oil. These determine the drug's medicinal use. It has a combined expectorant action, caused by the saponins, and soothing, healing action, due to the mucilaginous component. The pigments and flavonoid glycoside hesperin give the drug its bactericidal and anti-inflammatory action, to which the essential oil, albeit present only in minute quantity, also contributes. The drug is a tried-and-tested remedy for coughs occurring in chronic bronchitis and is therefore also a component of numerous herbal teas used in the treatment of chest colds and diseases associated with chilling and accompanied by coughs. It is used in the form of an infusion prepared from one tablespoon of the compressed drug to one cup of water to be taken two to five times daily. The infusion may be sweetened with honey. The drug also has mild antispasmodic and diuretic properties, which are of particular use in pediatrics. Only occasionally is the drug used externally. It is recommended as a cleansing treatment for inflammation of the large intestine, internal haemorrhoids, and may be applied externally in the form of a compress to varicose ulcers. For these purposes it is used as an infusion prepared from five tablespoons of the drug to one litre of previously boiled water. The drug from the flowers of the related Orange Mullein (*Verbascum phlomoides*) has the same properties. Small-flowered species of Mullein are not gathered.

4

Large-flowered Mullein (1) is a herb of sunny hillsides, pastureland and clearings. In the first year it forms a basal rosette of large, thick, flaky-felted leaves. In the second year it produces a tall stem up to two metres high terminated by a spike of large, symmetrical, five-petalled flowers with rotate, pale yellow corolla. Small-flowered mulleins (2) and their numerous hybrids are not suitable for the purposes of the drug market because they contain insufficient amounts of active principles. This is why the flowers of *Verbascum nigrum* (3), with bright

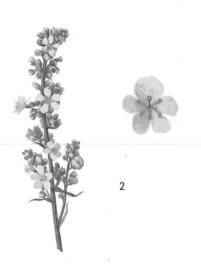

2

yellow corollas about two centimetres across and shaggy, violet stamens, are not collected. All mulleins are very ornamental. *Verbascum phoeniceum* with dark violet, medium-size flowers (4) is an attractive species.

3

1

Vervain
Verbena officinalis L.

The illustrated Vervain belongs to a genus comprising some two hundred species, distributed in North and South America. It has been known in Europe since ancient times, mainly in the warmer regions. In the Middle Ages it was considered to have extraordinary medicinal powers. For example the German name for the plant is derived from the belief that it heals wounds caused by iron weapons. Nowadays it is occasionally investigated as a promising medicinal herb. Its importance, however, is overrated. The chief active principle of the drug, which consists of the dried stems cut at the beginning of flowering, is the glycoside verbenalin plus bitter principles, mucilage, tannins, and a small amount of a lemon-scented essential oil. In folk medicine it is justifiably recommended as a diuretic and an aid to digestion. It is also reputed to have a specifically constipating action. Current central European phytotherapy, however, is reserved in its use of the drug. It is far more popular in southern Europe where it is also recommended as a tonic remedy for exhaustion and depression. It corrects minor menstrual irregularities, its diuretic properties eliminate oedemas caused by cardio-vascular disorders, and it is recommended in the treatment of inflammation of the spleen and liver. The drug is used in the form of an infusion or briefly boiled decoction prepared from one teaspoon of the crumbled drug to one cup water and taken three to five times daily. Externally it is used in the form of compresses applied to stubborn wounds and ulcers. It is only a rather mild substitute for the closely related *Vitex agnus-castus* L. in the alleviation of premenstrual migrains.

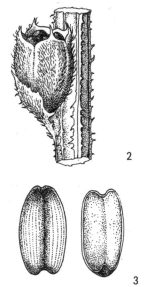

2

3

Vervain (1) is an annual or perennial herb reaching a height of about half a metre, with an erect, stiff, four-angled stem loosely branched towards the top. The opposite, grey-green leaves are lobed, stiff and roughly hairy. It grows on field boundaries and in waste places only in warmer regions. The small flowers, apparent from July until August and arranged in long clusters, grow from the leaf joints of minute stemless bracts. The calyx is tubular and glandular, the corolla indistinctly two-lobed and generally coloured pale violet. The fruits (2) are long cylindrical nutlets (3 — view from both sides). Often grown for ornament are the garden hybrids *Verbena × hybrida* whose variety of colours ranks them among the loveliest of flowers. They are native to South America.

allongées (3 — vus des deux côtés). Les
hybrides de jardin *Verbena* × *hybrida*,
que la variété de couleurs place parmi
les plus jolies fleurs, sont souvent
cultivés pour l'ornement. Ils sont
originaires d'Amérique du Sud.

1

Wild Pansy, Heartsease
Viola tricolor L.

Violaceae

The genus *Viola,* numbering as many as four hundred and fifty species, is the largest in the whole family and its members are distributed practically worldwide. Wild Pansy grows in Europe, western Siberia, the Middle East and north Africa, often as a field weed. The flowering stems, which are used medicinally, are obtained only from plants growing in the wild. The constituents include mainly saponins, flavonoid glycosides and ancillary substances. The drug's effect is increased by the presence of mucilage and tannins, and is used internally as well as externally. Internally it is used mainly in the treatment of inflammation of the upper respiratory passages due to its saponin content. The drug's diuretic and antiseptic properties are used in herbal teas to treat infections of the urinary tract. The drug is used in the form of an infusion prepared from one teaspoon of the crumbled drug to one cup of water and steeped briefly, or from one tablespoon of the drug to a quarter of a litre of cold water, then steeped for eight hours. The dosage is two to four cups daily, taken after meals. Externally the drug is recommended in the form of compresses chiefly for skin diseases in small children, e. g. infant eczemas and dermatoses. Compresses are prepared by soaking a gauze pad in one of the above-mentioned infusions. It is recommended to supplement external treatment with internal treatment, i. e. by taking one cup of the infusion twice a day. According to R. F. Weiss the infusion may be used in place of water in the preparation of food for infants. In the case of adults it must be taken into account that treatment will necessarily take longer, although the drug's action is equally reliable.

2

Wild Pansy (1) is an annual or biennial herb of weedy character. It grows in fields, on ridges, by waysides and in waste places. The flowering period is from April until October. It has partly creeping, ascending, often much-branched stems that reach a height of twenty centimetres. The petals are pale yellow, or else the two upper petals are violet blue and the three lower ones have dark longitudinal stripes; the lowest petal has a long blunt spur (2). Wild Pansy occurs in several races, all of which may be gathered for the drug market for all have equivalent properties. Sweet Violet (*Viola odorata* L.) is also used medicinally but is of greater importance in perfumery. Some species have been practically exterminated by indiscriminate

1

3

collecting and are therefore protected by
law. One such is *Viola lutea* subsp.
sudetica — a perennial mountain violet
with deep yellow flowers (3).

Common Mistletoe
Viscum album L. subsp. *album*   Loranthaceae

The genus *Viscum* numbers some sixty-five species found mainly in Africa, Asia and Australia. Three subspecies of parasitic Mistletoe — one parasitic on broad-leaved trees and two on coniferous trees — are native to Europe. Common Mistletoe is the one that interests us most. The leafy tips of young twigs without the thick basal stems and without the berries are the parts used medicinally. These are collected only in the wild and therefore include, albeit in small quantities, also mistletoe subspecies parasitic on coniferous trees — subsp. *abietis* and subsp. *austriacum*. The drug contains toxic polypeptids and viscotoxins, as well as lectins, triterpenic acids, acetylcholine and glycosidically found substances. These constituents are useful for the treatment of less severe cases of high blood pressure and although the drug is a mild medicament for the treatment of this condition it far surpasses synthetic preparations that cause undesirable side effects. Mistletoe is used in the form of an infusion prepared from one teaspoon of the crushed drug steeped briefly in one cup water and taken two to three times daily; the drug may also be steeped for a longer period, i. e., eight hours. R. F. Weiss recommends combining equal parts of the drug from Mistletoe, Hawthorn and Balm to prepare an infusion from two teaspoons of the mixture to one cup of water, sipped in the morning and evening. Besides having a favourable action on high blood pressure and arteriosclerosis the drug shows promise of *possible* use in checking malignant growths in the light of recent research. It is also a raw material for the commercial production of pharmaceutical preparations.

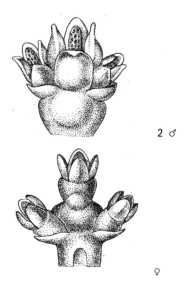

2 ♂

♀

Mistletoe (1) is a parasitic, evergreen shrublet, with both male and female plants, that grows on the branches of broad-leaved as well as coniferous trees, in dense clusters. The stems, which branch by repeated forking, are rounded and brittle. The leaves are persistent, oblong-ovate, with entire margin and thickly leathery. The male and female (2) flowers are small, yellowish-green, and inconspicuous. The fruit is the size of a pea and resembles a berry. In plants that are parasitic on broad-leaved trees the fruits are white, in those that are parasitic on coniferous trees they are

218

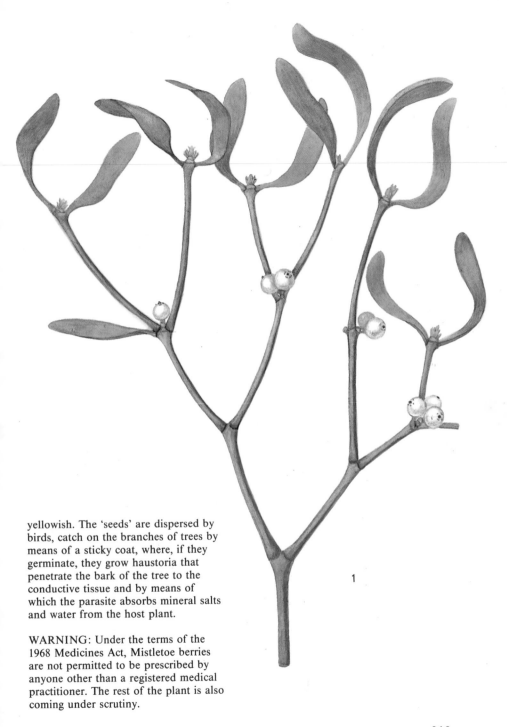

yellowish. The 'seeds' are dispersed by birds, catch on the branches of trees by means of a sticky coat, where, if they germinate, they grow haustoria that penetrate the bark of the tree to the conductive tissue and by means of which the parasite absorbs mineral salts and water from the host plant.

WARNING: Under the terms of the 1968 Medicines Act, Mistletoe berries are not permitted to be prescribed by anyone other than a registered medical practitioner. The rest of the plant is also coming under scrutiny.

1

Index of Common Names

Numbers in bold type refer to main entries

Index of Scientific Names
Numbers in bold type refer to main entries

222